CONCATENATED CODES

CONCATENATED CODES

G. DAVID FORNEY, JR.

 RESEARCH MONOGRAPH No. 37
THE M.I.T. PRESS, CAMBRIDGE, MASSACHUSETTS

Foreword

This is the thirty-seventh volume in the M.I.T. Research Monograph Series published by the M.I.T. Press. The objective of this series is to contribute to the professional literature a number of significant pieces of research, larger in scope than journal articles but normally less ambitious than finished books. We believe that such studies deserve a wider circulation than can be accomplished by informal channels, and we hope that this form of publication will make them readily accessible to research organizations, libraries, and independent workers.

HOWARD W. JOHNSON

Preface

The prime mover for coding research since 1948 has been Shannon's coding theorem, which promised negligibly low error probabilities at rates arbitrarily near capacity. Concatenation is a way of achieving such performance without requiring an impossibly complex decoder. It promises to be particularly useful whenever the high performance contemplated by the coding theorem is actually demanded, as on very expensive channels.

The greater part of the work reported here appeared in my thesis,† although its presentation has been completely revised. Results concerning the decoding of BCH codes (Appendix B) and generalized minimum distance decoding (Chapter 3) which, while useful in concatenation, are also of independent interest, have been reported in separate articles.‡ Other results which may have interest apart from concatenation appear in Chapter 2, where we discuss the structure and properties of BCH codes and derive the weight distribution of Reed-Solomon codes. However, the central results are those of Chapter 4, where we analyze the performance of concatenated codes and exhibit realizable codes capable of achieving low error probabilities at rates near the capacity of a memoryless channel. Chapter 5 supports this theory with computational results on the performance of representative schemes.

† "Concatenated Codes," Sc.D. thesis, Department of Electrical Engineering, Massachusetts Institute of Technology, Cambridge, Massachusetts, June, 1965; reproduced in Technical Report 440, Massachusetts Institute of Technology Research Laboratory of Electronics, 1966.

‡ "On Decoding BCH Codes," *IEEE Trans. Information Theory*, **IT-11**, 549–557 (1965); "Generalized Minimum Distance Decoding," *IEEE Trans. Information Theory* (Los Angeles Symposium) **IT-12**, 125–131 (1966).

The story being told here is a simple one, as the presentation attempts to reflect. By making the monograph nearly self-contained, I have hoped to render it accessible to students with minimal acquaintance with communication theory as well as to the graduate engineer who has not followed the details of current research. Believing that in an engineering work the conceptual framework is all-important but that rigor is not, I have skimped on details of proofs which did not seem to contribute insight, while spending more time than I might on discussions of the general structure of communications systems and on previously known results, wherever possible attempting an original treatment. But, while rigor is largely ignored, the powerful and illuminating concepts of the mathematical disciplines—symmetry, linearity, convexity, asymptotic limit behavior—are freely appropriated.

Properly to acknowledge the help of all who have contributed to a work like this is next to impossible. The referee noted some influences of "the local intellectual climate," which, if true, is a fine compliment; I doubt that I could have produced this work anywhere but at the Massachusetts Institute of Technology, where the comprehensive course content, the stimulation of ongoing research, and the readily available friendly encouragement and incisive criticism constitute an excellent climate for research. I am particularly indebted to John McR. Wozencraft, who as my thesis adviser first encouraged me to investigate concatenation, and to Robert G. Gallager, whose close attention was the greatest help. Robert Kennedy was an interested and responsive reader. The RLE Document Room provided cheerful bibliographic assistance, while the time-sharing facility of the Massachusetts Institute of Technology Computation Center was invaluable in the search for good codes of Chapter 5. The financial assistance provided by a National Science Foundation Graduate Fellowship and a Lincoln Laboratory Staff Associateship during my graduate career is gratefully acknowledged. At Codex Corporation, I have been fortunate in being able freely to pursue these investigations under the stimulus of practical requirements; credit for this happy circumstance is due to Arthur Kohlenberg, a sympathetic friend, and to the support of the NASA Ames Research Center, under Contract NAS 2-2874. Thanks are also due to Marilyn Churchill, who was good enough to type the manuscript. Finally, I have the great good fortune to have as helpmate my Dede, who assumed the difficult role of graduate student wife with model grace and understanding. And what we both owe our families is immeasurable.

Cambridge, Massachusetts   G. DAVID FORNEY, JR.
January, 1966

Contents

Preface   vii

1. Introduction   1

   1.1 Definitions; the Coding Theorem and Its Deficiencies
        1
   1.2 The Idea of Concatenation; Plan of the Monograph
        5
   1.3 Modulation; Likelihoods; Motivation for GMD
        7
   1.4 Channels with Memory   10
   1.5 Concatenation with Convolutional Codes   10
        References   11

2. Reed-Solomon and BCH Codes   12

   2.1 Finite Fields   12
   2.2 Linear Codes   16
        2.2.1 *The Weight Distribution of Maximum Codes*   19
   2.3 Reed-Solomon Codes   21
        2.3.1 *Cyclic* RS *Codes*   22
        2.3.2 *Encoding and Decoding* RS *Codes*   26
        2.3.3 *Shortened* RS *Codes*   27
        2.3.4 *Another Treatment of* RS *Codes*   28
   2.4 BCH Codes   29
        References   34

ix

3. Generalized Minimum Distance Decoding   35

    3.1 Decoding Binary Signals   35
         3.1.1 *Maximum Likelihood Decoding*   37
         3.1.2 *Hamming Distance Decoding*   40
         3.1.3 *Generalized Minimum Distance Decoding*   43
         3.1.4 *Bounds on Probability of Not Decoding Correctly*   47
         3.1.5 *Binary Antipodal Signaling with White Gaussian Noise*   51
    3.2 Decoding Nonbinary Signals   55
         3.2.1 *List Decoding*   59
    3.3 Discussion   61
         References   62

4. Theoretical Performance of Concatenated Codes   63

    4.1 Coding Theorems for Superchannels   63
         4.1.1 *Detailed Statement of the Coding Theorem*   64
         4.1.2 *Best and Worst Channels*   69
         4.1.3 *Coding Theorems for Concatenated Codes*   74
         4.1.4 *Properties of Concatenation Exponents*   78
    4.2 Performance of RS Codes as Outer Codes   83
    4.3 Discussion   88
         References   90

5. Computed Performance of Concatenated Codes   91

    5.1 Coding for Equierror Channels   92
         5.1.1 *Discussion*   98
    5.2 Coding for Gaussian Channels   99
         5.2.1 *Discussion*   102
    5.3 Summary   105
         Reference   105

Appendix A. The Coding Theorem for Discrete Memoryless Channels   106
         References   113

Appendix B. Decoding BCH Codes   114

    B.1 The Basic Algorithm   114
         B.1.1 *Syndromes*   115
         B.1.2 *Finding the Error Locators*   116
         B.1.3 *Determining Error and Erasure Values*   118
         B.1.4 *Complexity of Implementation*   119

B.2 Modifications of the Basic Algorithm   121
B.3 An Algorithm for GMD Decoding   125
    B.3.1 *The Algorithm*   126
    References   129

Appendix C. Performance of List Decoding   130

Appendix D. Formulas for Computation   134
    D.1 The Outer Decoder   134
    D.2 The Inner Decoder   136
    D.3 Modulation on a Gaussian Channel   139
    References   142

Author Index   143

Subject Index   145

1. Introduction

1.1 Definitions; the Coding Theorem and Its Deficiencies

Traditionally, one begins a work on coding theory with a discussion of the coding theorem. This custom will be honored here—not for the sake of form, but because the coding theorem has directly motivated much of the research in the field it created. For almost twenty years, since Shannon[3] announced this remarkable result, it has stimulated extraordinary effort. Yet, although our understanding of the coding theorem has been much refined, it cannot be said that we have satisfactory answers to the questions it raises which, from a practical viewpoint, are the most fundamental.

This situation arises from the coding theorem's being an existence theorem. It demonstrates that a certain standard of performance can be obtained by some coding scheme, but fails to specify a particular code which achieves this standard or an encoding and decoding method which is reasonable to consider for implementation. To remedy this deficiency has been the goal of much of the work in coding theory.

In Appendix A we present the coding theorem for block codes on discrete memoryless channels in its most modern form; we shall now briefly summarize the character of this result, after introducing some basic definitions.

By a *channel* is meant some medium which is available to both transmitter and receiver and which is the sole means of communication between them. A single *use* of the channel consists in the transmitter acting on the channel in some way and the receiver observing some characteristic of the channel which reflects the action of the transmitter.

1

In the case of a *discrete* channel, the transmitter is limited to one of a finite set of J actions called the *inputs* x_j, $1 \le j \le J$; correspondingly, the receiver distinguishes only between K classes of observations called *outputs* y_k, $1 \le k \le K$. The relation between inputs and outputs is in general probabilistic; the channel is characterized by specifying $\Pr(\mathbf{y} \mid \mathbf{x})$ for every *input sequence* $\mathbf{x} = \{x_i\} = (x_1, x_2, \cdots)$ and *output sequence* $\mathbf{y} = (y_1, y_2, \cdots)$. The channel is by definition *memoryless* if for every such pair of input and output sequences

$$\Pr[(y_1, y_2, \cdots) \mid (x_1, x_2, \cdots)] = \Pr(y_1 \mid x_1)\Pr(y_2 \mid x_2)\cdots$$

A discrete memoryless channel is then completely characterized by its *transition probability matrix*

$$p_{kj} = \Pr(y_k \mid x_j), \qquad 1 \le j \le J, \quad 1 \le k \le K.$$

By a *block code* of *length* N and *rate* R for such a channel is meant a set of e^{NR} input sequences or *code words* of length N:

$$\mathbf{x}_m = \{x_{mi}\} = (x_{m1}, x_{m2}, \cdots, x_{mN}), \qquad 1 \le m \le e^{NR}.$$

Here we have implicitly defined the units of rate to be *nats*, rather than the more common *bits*. Except where specified, we shall use nats in this work; conversions can be made by use of the relationships

$$1 \text{ nat} = \log_2 e \, (=1.4) \text{ bits};$$
$$1 \text{ bit} = \ln 2 \, (=0.69) \text{ nat};$$

where ln indicates the natural (base e) logarithm. Another useful measure of rate comes from observing that, if J is the total number of inputs, J^N is the total number of input sequences of length N, so that the rate is bounded by

$$R \le R_{\max} = \ln J.$$

It is frequently convenient to use the *dimensionless rate* r, defined by

$$r = \frac{R}{R_{\max}};$$

r is seen to lie between zero and one. In terms of r the number of words in the code can be expressed as

$$e^{NR} = e^{NrR_{\max}} = J^{rN}.$$

An *encoder* is a mechanical device which accepts one of e^{NR} commands from a data source and generates the corresponding input sequence for transmission over the channel. Commonly the data source will be a continuous stream of binary data; for every $NR \log_2 e$ bits the encoder generates a code word. A *decoder* is a device which observes an output sequence of length N, processes this sequence, and presents the result to the data sink or user in the form desired. Commonly the user wants to know which code word was transmitted; if the encoder input was $NR \log_2 e$ bits, the decoder output will be $NR \log_2 e$ bits also, called an *estimate*. The event in which the estimate is not identical with the input code word is called an *error*.

The *probability of error* $\Pr(\mathscr{E})$ depends on the code, the channel, and the decoder's processing strategy. If the decoder is deterministic, then its strategy is describable as a mapping from the set of all received sequences $\mathbf{y}$ to the code words $\mathbf{x}_m$, and is specified by listing the sets Y_m of sequences $\mathbf{y}$ which result in a decoder estimate of $\mathbf{x}_m$. If it is assumed that the code, channel, and decoder are as specified and that all code words are equally likely, the probability of error is

$$\Pr(\mathscr{E}) = \sum_{m=1}^{e^{NR}} \Pr(\mathbf{x}_m)\Pr(\mathbf{y} \text{ not in } Y_m \mid \mathbf{x}_m \text{ transmitted})$$

$$= e^{-NR} \sum_{m=1}^{e^{NR}} \sum_{\mathbf{y} \notin Ym} \Pr(\mathbf{y} \mid \mathbf{x}_m).$$

The probability of error is therefore minimized if the decoder implements the *maximum likelihood decision rule*, for which *

$$\mathbf{y} \in Y_m \text{ iff } \Pr(\mathbf{y} \mid \mathbf{x}_m) > \Pr(\mathbf{y} \mid \mathbf{x}_{m'}), \quad \text{all } m' \neq m.$$

The stunning result known as the coding theorem is the following. Every discrete memoryless channel has a *capacity* C such that for all rates R less than C there exist codes of rate R which with maximum likelihood decoding have arbitrarily small probability of error. Few readers of this monograph will need to be told of the sensation evoked by the announcement of this theorem nor to be reminded of its implications.

We now know that the probability of error can be made to decrease exponentially with the block length. In Appendix A it is demonstrated that there exists a block code of rate R and length N such that

$$\Pr(\mathscr{E}) \leq e^{-NE_L(R)},$$

where $E_L(R)$, called the *lower-bound error exponent*, is a function of R which is specified by the transition probability matrix of the channel and

---

* The question of what to do in the boundary regions where the *a posteriori* probabilities are equal for two code words is of no significance; an error may always be assumed.

is positive for all rates $R < C$. We also know that for every code of rate R and length N

$$\Pr(\mathscr{E}) \geq e^{-N[E_U(R)+o(1)]},$$

where $o(1)$ is a function which approaches zero as N becomes very large, and $E_U(R)$ is called the *upper-bound error exponent*; $E_U(R) \rightarrow 0$ as $R \rightarrow C$, so that the channel capacity is precisely known. We discuss the character of $E_L(R)$ and $E_U(R)$ in more detail in Section 4.1.1.

On the basis of the coding theorem one could imagine finding by trial and error a code with performance meeting the standard of the theorem, and implementing it with an encoder which stored the e^{NR} code words in a dictionary and a maximum likelihood decoder capable of computing $\Pr(\mathbf{y} \mid \mathbf{x}_m)$ for each code word. But in such a scheme the size of the encoder and the number of computations required of the decoder would each be increasing exponentially with the block length N, so that, while the probability of error would decrease exponentially with N, it would decrease only weakly algebraically with the complexity. That is, if the complexity $G \sim e^{NR}$, while $\Pr(\mathscr{E}) \sim e^{-NE(R)}$, $\Pr(\mathscr{E}) \sim G^{-E(R)/R}$.

One is therefore faced with the problem of finding a code and an associated decoding scheme such that the complexity of the encoder and decoder required to implement the scheme increases much more slowly than exponentially with N. The introduction of linear codes, which we shall discuss in Chapter 2, essentially solves the encoding problem for block codes by yielding a class of codes which can be encoded in encoders of complexity linear in N; furthermore, if there is symmetry between the inputs, as there normally is in channels of practical interest, codes in this class can meet the standard of performance of the coding theorem. Another type of code with these properties is the convolutional or recurrent type; these codes have no block structure, and are largely ignored in this work.

Two approaches to the problem of reducing decoder complexity can be distinguished. The first, sometimes called probabilistic, looks for a more efficient way of implementing something like maximum likelihood decoding than simple comparison; the outstanding result of this approach is sequential decoding, which is suitable for convolutional codes. However, although an eminently practical scheme, sequential decoding is bedeviled by a variability in number of decoding computations which necessitates buffer storage, the probability of whose overflow decreases only weakly algebraically with its size[5]; furthermore, sequential decoding is limited to rates below a certain rate R_{comp} (defined in Section 4.1.1) which is less than capacity. The second approach, sometimes called algebraic, depends on choosing a code based on the structures of modern algebra to facilitate the development of an efficient decoding algorithm; the outstanding result of this approach is the class of BCH codes, which we discuss in the next chapter. However, though the BCH codes of moderate length are useful codes, as the block length becomes large, the BCH codes are, as far as we know, useless, in a sense to be made precise in the last paragraph of Chapter 2.

In this monograph we consider an approach based on the concept of concatenation, to be elucidated in the next section. Concatenation combines the algebraic and probabilistic approaches to get very long codes for which the probability of error on memoryless channels decreases exponentially with block length, while decoder complexity increases only as a small power of the block length. This happy result holds for all rates less than capacity, as we shall show in Chapter 4. In this sense it brings us within hailing distance of the promised land sighted by Shannon so long ago.

1.2   The Idea of Concatenation; Plan of the Monograph

Recall our description of a block coding scheme for a discrete memoryless channel, and imagine how it would appear to an observer who could see only the data source and data sink. For each block, the data source would submit one of e^{NR} commands, and the data sink would be given one of the e^{NR} decoder estimates. Generally the estimate would match the input, but occasional errors would occur. From this viewpoint, the encoder-channel-decoder would appear to be a discrete memoryless *superchannel* with e^{NR} inputs and e^{NR} outputs. One immediately sees that it is possible to design a block code of length n and dimensionless rate r for this superchannel. But now, in terms of uses of the original channel, one has created a block code of over-all length $N_0 = nN$, with e^{nNrR} words, and thus of over-all rate $R_0 = rR$. The encoder for this very long block code happens to consist of two encoders back-to-back and the decoder of two decoders, suitable for much shorter codes. These ideas are illustrated in Figure 1.1, where we have called the two codes *inner* and *outer*.

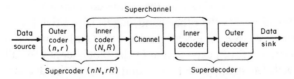

Figure 1.1   Concatenation concepts. n, outer-code length; N, inner-code length; $nN = N_0 =$ over-all length; r, outer-code dimensionless rate; R, inner-code rate; $rR = R_0 =$ over-all rate.

Although it serves to introduce concatenation, the conceptual separation of the two codes is artificial. As engineers, we want to design both codes simultaneously to get the best over-all performance with the least over-all complexity. We want to know answers to questions like these: What are the best codes to use? Can we reduce the decoding load or increase performance by letting one decoder help the other? Most importantly, what sort of performance is obtainable, at the cost of what complexity?

We find that use of codes of the BCH type is quite satisfactory, though we nowhere prove that they are best. In particular, we always use as an outer code a Reed-Solomon (RS) code. Reed-Solomon codes are nonbinary BCH codes which, whenever they can be used, are optimal, in a sense to be made precise in Chapter 2. Furthermore, RS codes admit an efficient decoding algorithm based on their algebraic structure, which we discuss in Appendix B. Chapter 2 gives a rapid introduction to BCH codes, with emphasis on RS codes.

In Chapter 3 we consider the possibility of the inner decoder passing along something more to the outer decoder than just its best guess. In particular, we let the inner decoder add to its estimate a real number which indicates how reliable it supposes its estimate to be. We show how such information can be efficiently used by the outer decoder in an algebraic decoding scheme in a method we call generalized minimum distance (or GMD) decoding. We also consider other methods of passing along reliability information: erasures, which we treat as highly quantized reliability information, and lists, which we consider only to discard. We develop bounds on performance with these different possibilities, and show that GMD can improve performance without much increase in complexity.

In Chapter 4 we investigate the performance obtainable with concatenation; we find that, with a Reed-Solomon outer code and GMD decoder, we can achieve

$$\Pr(\mathscr{E}) \leq e^{-N_0 E_C(R_0)},$$

where $E_C(R_0)$ is called the *concatenation exponent*, and N_0 and R_0 are the over-all length and rate of the concatenation scheme. It turns out that $E_C(R)$ is less than $E_L(R)$, so that some sacrifice is involved in going to concatenation. On the other hand, $E_C(R)$ is positive for all rates less than capacity, so that the essential feature that makes the coding theorem so provocative—$\Pr(\mathscr{E})$ exponential in the block length for all $R < C$— is preserved. Most important, the complexity of the decoder increases proportionately only to a small power of the block length, N_0.

Finally, computations in Chapter 5 support these theoretical results and give some insight into the practical design of concatenated codes.

1.3 Modulation; Likelihoods; Motivation for GMD

Nature rarely gives us a discrete channel. It is true that it is occasionally necessary to design communications terminals for channels which must be treated as discrete, such as a cable with binary repeaters. More generally, though, the channel is simply a piece of wire or of space, which we make discrete by our choice of modulator, demodulator, and detector. Within the framework of concatenation it is natural to consider these devices as additional stages of concatenation and to draw the moral, which should have been plain all along, that coding and modulation ought to be designed together to maximize performance while minimizing complexity.

A *modulator* is a device that accepts one of J commands from a data source or encoder and generates a corresponding signal for the physical channel. The distinction between a demodulator and a detector is sometimes hazy, but for our purposes it shall be the following. A *demodulator* is a device whose output is the earliest quantity in the receiver chain to which we can possibly gain access; a *detector* is a device which accepts this output and prepares from it a signal in a format useful to the decoder or, in the absence of a decoder, to the data sink.

The purpose of this distinction is to emphasize that there is often information available in the receiver which is thrown away by the detector because the data sink or decoder cannot use it. For example, it frequently happens that, with binary modulation, the output of the demodulator is a voltage which may be anywhere within some range. If the decoder is such that it can handle only binary data, the detector must test whether the voltage is above or below some threshold, and deliver a "1" or a "0" accordingly, with no indication whether its decision was borderline or clear-cut. The use of an erasure output X whenever the voltage is within some null zone around the threshold, is one way to ameliorate this deficiency; the GMD approach of Chapter 3 is still better.

The detector need not throw away information at all. Let the output of the demodulator be y and suppose that the output of the detector is a set of J likelihoods y_j,

$$y_j = \Pr(y \mid x_j), \qquad 1 \le j \le J,$$

where the x_j are the possible signals. Such a detector we call a *likelihood detector*. Now compare the memoryless channel which has the x_j as inputs and y as output with that which has the x_j as inputs and the y_j as outputs. If we were to code for the former channel and use maximum likelihood decoding, we would form

$$\Pr(\mathbf{y} \mid \mathbf{x}_m) = \Pr(y_1 \mid x_{m1})\Pr(y_2 \mid x_{m2}) \cdots$$

for all code words $\mathbf{x}_m$. But we can still do this with the outputs of the likelihood detector and so achieve the same performance with any code. It follows that the error exponents for these two channels are the same, and thus their capacities. We can therefore say that *a likelihood detector is information lossless.* In the language of statistical decision theory, the likelihoods are sufficient statistics, in that they contain all information in y relevant to choosing between any hypotheses regarding the x_j. Without loss of generality, we may always assume the demodulator followed by a likelihood detector, which, like a finely quantized analog-to-digital converter, puts the output in a convenient format without affecting its information content.

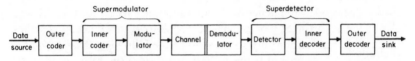

Figure 1.2   Concatenation with modulation.

We now return to the concatenation scheme of the previous section, which we have redrawn in Figure 1.2 to show a modulator, demodulator, and detector. From the viewpoint of the outer coder, the inner coder and modulator are together simply a modulator, and to the outer decoder the detector and inner decoder are simply a detector; on the other hand, to the inner coder and decoder the outer coder and decoder are simply a data source and sink. Regardless of how many stages of concatenation there are, then, for any coder-decoder pair the situation may be given the general formulation of Figure 1.3: a source-coder-modulator-channel-demodulator-detector-decoder-sink chain.

Figure 1.3   General formulation for particular coder-decoder pair.

These fancy acrobatics with points of view are useful as exercises to prevent our making a too rigid division between modulation and coding theory. As an example of how coding may be used in a modulator, we might now mention an interesting special case. Let the detector be a likelihood detector, and let the decoder form for each code word $\mathbf{x}_m$ the likelihoods y_m defined by

$$y_m = \Pr(\mathbf{y} \mid \mathbf{x}_m) = \Pr(y_1 \mid x_{m1})\Pr(y_2 \mid x_{m2}) \cdots \Pr(y_N \mid x_{mN}),$$

which it gives to the next outer decoder. If we call this a *likelihood decoder*, we see that a likelihood detector followed by a likelihood decoder is equivalent to a likelihood detector from the point of view of subsequent decoders or the data sink. As long as we use likelihood decoders, information is never destroyed; however, likelihood decoders become prohibitively complex when the number of code words e^{NR} is large. On the Gaussian channel, likelihood decoders are called word correlators; several have been built,[4] and we shall encounter their use in Chapter 5.

It is clear from Figure 1.3 that the interaction between any one decoder and the rest of the receiver is completely determined by the character of the information it receives from the detector and of that it must deliver to the sink. Let us define an *information packet* to be the output generated by a detector or decoder in a single operation. For a likelihood detector or decoder an information packet consists of J likelihoods; other possibilities are

1. An estimate;
2. An estimate, or an erasure;
3. An estimate, with a number indicating reliability;
4. A list of estimates, with or without associated reliabilities.

These are the possibilities which we said in the last section we would examine in Chapter 3. The function of a decoder is now seen to be to accept N information packets from the detector and to generate a single information packet for the sink.

The engineering problem may be regarded as the following. We would like to choose the modulator—which may include coders—and the detector—which may include decoders—to maximize the error exponent, and hence the capacity, of the resulting discrete channel. However, this will in general involve increasing the information content of the packets generated by the detector and the complexity of the modulator and detector; this competes with our desire to minimize the complexity of the decoder, which will in general involve decreasing the information content of these packets. A likelihood decoder destroys no information, but has complexity exponential in N. An ordinary algebraic decoder using packets of Type 1 (estimates only) has complexity proportional to a small power of N, as we show in Appendix B, but in such packets much information is lost. However, generalized minimum distance decoding, which uses packets of Type 3, requires little more complexity than an ordinary algebraic decoder, while preserving in some cases effectively all useful information, as we shall see in Chapters 3 and 4. Such packets are thus useful in solving the total problem, which is to design coding and modulation of the minimum total complexity to achieve a given standard of performance.

1.4   Channels with Memory

The difficulty of implementing decoders is one reason that coding is not used more often on today's communication circuits; a more important one is that almost all real channels (except, it seems, for a few space channels) are not memoryless. Typically, long periods of good channel behavior alternate with short noisy periods called *bursts*. The theoretical apparatus of coding theory remains applicable to such channels; in particular the coding theorem can be proved for a large class of channels with memory. However, the essentially error-free performance promised by the coding theorem depends upon the use of codes long enough that the probability of an error-causing statistical fluctuation is very small. On channels with memory, it may take very long codes indeed—perhaps longer than the sunspot cycle, some have suggested—to ensure that the probability of the noise behavior being anything but "typical" is very small.

An inefficient way of coping with a bursty channel is to design a code to be operable under the worst possible conditions. A better method is to use either feedback from the receiver or some sort of channel measurement to adapt the transmission rate to currently observed conditions, or to repeat data. Otherwise, some variation of a technique called *interlacing* or scrambling is usually envisioned. This method contemplates first encoding N input sequences of length n, and then transmitting the N first elements, the N second elements, and so forth, until all nN inputs are transmitted. Clearly a burst of length $b \leq N$ can affect no more than one element in each code word, so that the N received words will normally be decodable if the average burst length is small compared to N.

Concatenation obviously shares the burst-resistant properties of interlacing when the average burst length is small compared to the length of the inner code. Because of the difficulty of constructing adequate models of real channels with memory, it is not possible to pursue analysis of the burst resistance of concatenated codes, but it may be anticipated that this feature will prove useful in real applications.

1.5   Concatenation with Convolutional Codes

In this monograph we consider only block codes; however, the idea of concatenation is clearly general, and many other applications can be conceived. For example, a simple threshold decoder[2] can decode a binary convolutional code correctly when channel errors are scattered; when it makes a decoding error, however, such a decoder tends to make several errors before it becomes resynchronized. The data source and sink then see an ideal bursty channel in which no errors are made except in bursts. Very efficient codes are known which detect and correct bursts on such channels. Beginning from a quite different point of view, Gallager[1] has invented a clever scheme which combines the threshold decoder and burst corrector into a single device, in which with high probability the threshold decoder itself detects the onset of a burst.

As we have mentioned, sequential decoding of convolutional codes is a useful high-performance technique. In the absence of a feedback channel, one must ordinarily separate data into long blocks independent of one another, since otherwise, when the buffer storage overflows, decoding must halt. With data blocks so separated, an overflow can cause the loss of no more than one block, for decoding can be begun again on the next block. One can then imagine using such blocks as inner code words and a Reed-Solomon code as an outer code, using the technique suitable for much-shortened RS codes of Section 2.3.3 to simplify instrumentation. The RS code would be used only for erasure-correction. If each of the inner code words were decoded more or less simultaneously, the outer code could be used to help a few at a time over humps of difficult error patterns. It appears that, besides increasing performance, such a scheme would reduce the variability in computation which is the bane of sequential decoding, and perhaps permit use of the technique above its present limit R_{comp}.

Undoubtedly the reader will find other applications of the idea of concatenation in the areas in which he is interested.

References

1. Codex Corp., Technical Bulletin No. 5, Watertown, Massachusetts, 1965.
2. J. L. Massey, *Threshold Decoding*, M.I.T. Press, Cambridge, Massachusetts, 1963.
3. C. E. Shannon and W. Weaver, *The Mathematical Theory of Communication*, University of Illinois Press, Urbana, Illinois, 1949. Also in *Bell System Tech. J.*, **27**, 379–423 and 623–656 (1948).
4. A. J. Viterbi, in *Digital Communications with Space Applications*, S. W. Golomb, ed., Prentice-Hall, Englewood Cliffs, New Jersey, 1964, pp. 131–133; M. E. Mitchell, "Simple Decoders and Correlators for Cyclic Error-Correcting Codes," *IEEE Trans. on Commun. Systems*, **CS-10**, 284–290 (1962).
5. J. McR. Wozencraft and I. M. Jacobs, *Principles of Communication Engineering*, John Wiley & Sons, Inc., New York, 1965, pp. 446–452.

2. Reed-Solomon and BCH Codes

This chapter is primarily intended to give the reader with little previous background direct access to the important class of BCH codes, with emphasis on the nonbinary Reed-Solomon codes.

The reader who is already thoroughly versed in this field may nonetheless be interested in our novel presentation and in the results on the structure and properties of RS codes, including their weight distribution. Those concerned with implementing BCH decoders may find our detailed consideration of decoding algorithms useful; these appear in Appendix B, but are summarized in Section 2.3.2.

Our presentation single-mindedly omits all but the essentials needed to understand BCH codes. The reader interested in a more rounded exposition based on their cyclic properties is referred to the comprehensive and still timely book by Peterson.[8] The treatment of finite fields which follows will be unsatisfactory to the reader who desires some depth of understanding about the properties we assert; Artin[1] is a widely recommended mathematical text, while Carmichael's Chapter IX[3] is an elegant and economical exposition.

2.1 Finite Fields

Mathematically, the finite field $GF(q)$ consists of q elements which can be added, subtracted, multiplied, and divided almost like real numbers. There is always a field element called zero (0), which has the property that any field element β plus or minus zero is β. There is also an element called one (1), such that $\beta \cdot 1 = \beta$; furthermore, $\beta \cdot 0 = 0$. If β is not zero, it has a multiplicative inverse β^{-1} which is that unique field element which satisfies the equation $\beta \cdot \beta^{-1} = 1$; division by β is accomplished by multiplication by β^{-1}. The inverse of 1 is 1.

The simplest examples of finite fields are the integers modulo a prime number p. For instance, take $p = 5$; then there are five elements in the field, which we shall write I, II, III, IV, and V to distinguish them from the integers to which they correspond. Addition, subtraction, and multiplication are carried out by converting these numbers to their integer equivalents and doing arithmetic modulo 5. For instance, I + III = IV, since $1 + 3 = 4 \bmod 5$; III + IV = II, since $3 + 4 = 2 \bmod 5$; I·III = III, since $1 \cdot 3 = 3 \bmod 5$; III·IV = II since $3 \cdot 4 = 2 \bmod 5$. Table 2.1 gives the complete addition and multiplication tables for $GF(5)$.

TABLE 2.1   Arithmetic in $GF(5)$

	Addition Table						Multiplication Table			
+	I	II	III	IV	V	·	I	II	III	IV	V
I	II	III	IV	V	I	I	I	II	III	IV	V
II	III	IV	V	I	II	II	II	IV	I	III	V
III	IV	V	I	II	III	III	III	I	IV	II	V
IV	V	I	II	III	IV	IV	IV	III	II	I	V
V	I	II	III	IV	V	V	V	V	V	V	V

Note that $V + \beta = \beta$, if β is any member of the field; therefore V must be the zero element. (Also $V \cdot \beta = V$.) $I \cdot \beta = \beta$, so I must be the one element. Since $I \cdot I = II \cdot III = IV \cdot IV = I$, $I^{-1} = I$, $II^{-1} = III$, $III^{-1} = II$, and $IV^{-1} = IV$.

In Table 2.2 we have constructed by these rules a chart of the first five powers of the field elements. It is to be observed that in every case

TABLE 2.2   The Powers of the Field Elements

β	β^2	β^3	β^4	β^5
I	I	I	I	I
II	IV	III	I	II
III	IV	II	I	III
IV	I	IV	I	IV
V	V	V	V	V

$\beta^5 = \beta$, while for any β other than the zero element V, $\beta^4 = I$. Furthermore, both II and III have the property that their first four powers are distinct and therefore yield the four nonzero field elements. Therefore if we let α denote the element II, say, $I = \alpha^0 = \alpha^4$, $II = \alpha$, $III = \alpha^3$, and $IV = \alpha^2$, which gives us a convenient representation of the field elements for multiplication and division, in the same way that the logarithmic relationship $x = 10^{\log_{10} x}$ gives us a convenient representation of the real numbers for multiplication and division.

Table 2.3 displays the two representations of $GF(5)$ which are convenient for addition and multiplication. If β corresponds to a and α^b, and γ corresponds to c and α^d, then $\beta + \gamma \leftrightarrow (a + c) \bmod 5$, $\beta - \gamma \leftrightarrow (a - b) \bmod 5$, $\beta \cdot \gamma \leftrightarrow \alpha^{[(b + d) \bmod 4]}$, and $\beta\gamma^{-1} \leftrightarrow \alpha^{[(b - d) \bmod 4]}$, where $\leftrightarrow$ means "corresponds to" and the "mod 4" in the exponent arises since $\alpha^4 = \alpha^0 = 1$.

TABLE 2.3   Representations for $GF(5)$

	$+, -$	$\times, \div$
I	1	α^0
II	2	α^1
III	3	α^3
IV	4	α^2
V	0	0

The prime field of most practical interest is $GF(2)$, whose two elements are simply 0 and 1. Addition and multiplication tables for $GF(2)$ appear in Table 2.4.

TABLE 2.4   Tables for $GF(2)$

+	0	1	·	0	1
0	0	1	0	0	0
1	1	0	1	0	1

It can be shown that the general finite field $GF(q)$ has $q = p^m$ elements, where p is again a prime and m is an arbitrary integer. As with $GF(5)$, we find it possible to construct two representations of $GF(q)$, one convenient for addition, one for multiplication. For addition, an element β of $GF(q)$ is represented by a sequence of m integers, $b_1, b_2, \cdots, b_m$, which may be considered as elements of $GF(p)$. To add β to γ, we add b_1 to c_1, b_2 to c_2, and so forth, all modulo p, as in $GF(p)$. For multiplication, it is always possible to find a *primitive element* α such that the first $q - 1$ powers of α yield the $q - 1$ nonzero field elements. Thus $\alpha^{q-1} = \alpha^0 = 1$ (or else the first $q - 1$ powers would not be distinct), and multiplication is accomplished by adding exponents mod $(q - 1)$. We have also, if β is any nonzero element,

$$\beta^{q-1} = (\alpha^a)^{q-1} = (\alpha^{q-1})^a = 1^a = 1,$$

and thus for any β, zero or not, $\beta^q = \beta$.

Thus all that remains to specify the properties of $GF(q)$ is to make the one-to-one identification between the addition and multiplication representations. Though this is easily done by using polynomials with coefficients from $GF(p)$, it is not necessary to know precisely what this identification is to understand what follows. (In fact, avoiding this point is the essential simplification of our presentation.) We note only that the zero element must be represented for addition by a sequence of m zeroes, in order that $0 + \beta = \beta$.

As an example of the general finite field, we use $GF(4) = GF(2^2)$, for which an addition table, multiplication table, and representation table are displayed in Table 2.5.

TABLE 2.5   Tables for $GF(4)$

	Addition				Multiplication				Representations	
	0	1	a	b	0	1	a	b		$+, -$	$\times, \div$
0	0	1	a	b	0	0	0	0	0	00	0
1	1	0	b	a	0	1	a	b	1	01	α^0
a	a	b	0	1	0	a	b	1	a	10	α^1
b	b	a	1	0	0	b	1	a	b	11	α^2

Note that $GF(4)$ contains two elements which can be identified as the two elements of $GF(2)$, namely, 0 and 1. In this case $GF(2)$ is said to be a *subfield* of $GF(4)$. In general, $GF(q')$ is a subfield of $GF(q)$ if and only if $q = q'^b$, where b is an integer. In particular, if $q = p^m$, the prime field $GF(p)$ is a subfield of $GF(q)$, and p is said to be the characteristic of the field.

The prime field $GF(p)$ contains the 0 and 1 elements of $GF(p^m)$, and preserves its own rules of combination; in particular

$$\underbrace{1 + 1 + \cdots + 1}_{p \text{ times}} = p \bmod p = 0.$$

Let β then be any element of $GF(p^m)$; we have

$$p\beta = \beta + \beta + \cdots + \beta = \beta(1 + 1 + \cdots + 1) = \beta \cdot 0 = 0.$$

In particular, in a field of characteristic two ($p = 2$),

$$\beta + \beta = 0,$$

so that $\beta = -\beta$ and addition is the same as subtraction. For this reason minus signs are not used when the field has characteristic two.

Furthermore, by the binomial theorem,

$$(\beta + \gamma)^p = \beta^p + \binom{p}{1}\beta^{p-1}\gamma + \cdots + \binom{p}{p-1}\beta\gamma^{p-1} + \gamma^p;$$

but in this series every term but the first and last is multiplied by p and hence is equal to zero by the previous paragraph. It follows that, in a field of characteristic p,

$$(\beta + \gamma)^p = \beta^p + \gamma^p,$$

so that raising to the pth power is a linear operation. Hence raising to the pth power any number of times is linear:

$$(\beta + \gamma)^{p^k} = \beta^{p^k} + \gamma^{p^k}.$$

2.2 Linear Codes

We know from the coding theorem that codes containing an exponentially large number of code words are required to achieve an exponentially low probability of error. Linear codes[14] can contain such a great number of words, yet remain feasible to generate; they facilitate minimum distance decoding, as we shall see; finally, as a class they can be shown to contain members for which the coding theorem is satisfied, when the channel inputs are symmetric. They have therefore been the subject of the overwhelming majority of coding studies.

Assume that we have a channel with q inputs, where q is a prime power, so that we can identify the different inputs with the elements of a finite field $GF(q)$. A *word* $\mathbf{f}$ of length n consists of a sequence of n elements from $GF(q)$. We shall write $\mathbf{f} = (f_1, f_2, \cdots, f_n) = \{f_i\}$, where f_i occupies the ith *place*. The *weight* $w(\mathbf{f})$ of $\mathbf{f}$ is defined as the number of nonzero elements in $\mathbf{f}$.

A linear combination of two words $\mathbf{f}_1$ and $\mathbf{f}_2$ is written $\beta\mathbf{f}_1 + \gamma\mathbf{f}_2$, where β and γ are each elements of $GF(q)$, and where ordinary vectorial (that is, place-by-place) addition in $GF(q)$ is implied. For example, if $\mathbf{f}_1 = \{f_{1i}\}$ and $\mathbf{f}_2 = \{f_{2i}\}$, then $\mathbf{f}_1 - \mathbf{f}_2 = \{f_{1i} - f_{2i}\}$.

A *linear code* of length n is a subset of the q^n words of length n with the important property that *any linear combination of code words yields another code word*. A code is *nondegenerate* if all its words are different; we consider only such codes.

The Hamming distance, or simply *distance*, between two words is the number of places in which they differ; the *minimum distance* of a code is the minimum distance between any two code words. Saying that the distance between two words $\mathbf{f}_1$ and $\mathbf{f}_2$ is d is equivalent to saying that the weight of their difference, $w(\mathbf{f}_1 - \mathbf{f}_2)$, is d, since $\mathbf{f}_1 - \mathbf{f}_2$ will have zeroes in places in which and only in which the two words do not differ. In a linear code, moreover, $\mathbf{f}_1 - \mathbf{f}_2$ must be another code word $\mathbf{f}_3$, so that if there are two code words separated by distance d there is a code word of weight d, and vice versa. Excluding the all-zero, zero-weight word, which must appear in every linear code since $0 \cdot \mathbf{f}_1 + 0 \cdot \mathbf{f}_2$ is a valid linear combination of code words, *the minimum distance of a linear code is then the minimum weight of any of its words*.

We shall be interested in the properties of sets of j different places, or sets of *size j*, which will be defined with reference to a given code. If the j places are such that there is no code word but the all-zero word with zeroes in all j places, we say that these j places form a *non-null set* of size j for that code; otherwise they form a *null set*.

If there is a set of k places such that there is one and only one code word corresponding to each of the possible q^k assignments of elements from $GF(q)$ to those k places, then we call it an *information set*[11] of size k; thus any code with an information set of size k has exactly q^k code words. The remaining $n - k$ places form a *check set*. An information set must be a non-null set for otherwise there would be two or more words corresponding to the assignment of all zeroes to the information set.

We now show that all linear codes have an information set of size k, for some k, by showing the equivalence of the two statements: 1. There is an information set of size k for the code. 2. The smallest non-null set has size k. For an information set of size k implies q^k code words; to any set of size $k - 1$ or less there are no more than q^{k-1} different assignments, so there must be at least two distinct code words which are the same in those places; but then their difference, though not the all-zero word, is zero in those places, so that any set of size $k - 1$ or less is a null set. Conversely, if the smallest non-null set has size k, then all its subsets of $k - 1$ places are null sets; therefore there is a code word f which is zero in all but the pth place of the smallest non-null set, but is nonzero in the pth place. If $\mathbf{f}$ is such a code word with β in the pth place, then $\beta^{-1} \cdot \mathbf{f}$ is a code word with a one in the pth place and zeroes in the remaining places of the smallest non-null set. The k words with this property are called *generators*; clearly, their q^k linear combinations yield q^k code words distinct in the specified k places. (This is the property that makes linear codes easy to generate; we need store only the k generators in the encoder.) But there can be no more than q^k words in the code; otherwise all sets of size k would be null sets, by the foregoing arguments.

Thus the smallest non-null set must be an information set. In fact, every non-null set of size k is an information set, since to each of the q^k code words must correspond a different assignment of elements to those k places. We say such a code has k information symbols, $n - k$ check symbols, and dimensionless rate k/n, and call it an (n, k) code on $GF(q)$.

For a given n and k, it is generally desirable to use a code with as large a minimum distance as possible. If the minimum distance of a code is d, then the minimum weight of any nonzero code word is d, and the largest null set has size $n - d$. It follows that all sets of size $n - d + 1$ are non-null sets, so the smallest non-null set has size $n - d + 1$ or less. The number of information symbols must be $n - d + 1$ or less, and the number of check symbols $d - 1$ or greater. A code which has length n, minimum distance d, and exactly the maximum number of information symbols, $n - d + 1$, will be called a *maximum code*.[13]

In a maximum code all sets of size $n - d + 1$ are non-null sets and hence information sets; since these are the smallest non-null sets, all sets of size $n - d$ or less are null sets. If all sets of size $n - d + 1$ or greater are non-null sets, then there are no code words of weight $d - 1$ or less, so the code is maximum; *a code is maximum with minimum distance d if and only if every set of size $n - d + 1$ is an information set.* This dichotomy in sizes between null and non-null sets in maximum codes is the property which facilitates their analysis and in particular the calculation of their weight distribution in the next subsection.

For example, let us consider the code which consists of all words **f** which satisfy the equation

$$f_1 + f_2 + \cdots + f_n = \sum_{i=1}^{n} f_i = 0.$$

It is a linear code, since, if $\mathbf{f}_1$ and $\mathbf{f}_2$ satisfy this equation, $\mathbf{f}_3 = (\beta\mathbf{f}_1 + \gamma\mathbf{f}_2)$ also satisfies the equation. Let us assign elements from $GF(q)$ arbitrarily to all places but the pth. In order for there to be one and only one code word with these elements in these places, f_p must be the unique solution to

$$\sum_{i \neq p} f_i + f_p = 0, \quad \text{or} \quad f_p = - \sum_{i \neq p} f_i.$$

Clearly this specifies a unique f_p which solves the equation. Since p is arbitrary, every set of $n - 1$ places is thus an information set, so that this code is a maximum code with length n, $n - 1$ information symbols, and minimum distance 2.

2.2.1 The Weight Distribution of Maximum Codes. In general, the number of code words of given weight in a linear code is difficult or impossible to determine; for many codes even d, the minimum weight, is not accurately known. Surprisingly, determination of the weight distribution of a maximum code presents no problems.

Suppose a maximum code of length n and minimum distance d, with symbols from $GF(q)$; in such a code there are $n - d + 1$ information symbols, and, as we have seen, every set of $n - d + 1$ places must be an information set, which can be used to generate the complete set of code words.

Aside from the all-zero, zero-weight word, there are no code words of weight less than d. To find the number of code words of weight d, we reason as follows. Take an arbitrary set S of d places, and consider the set of all code words which have all zeroes in the remaining $n - d$ places. One of these words will be the all-zero word; the rest must have weight d, since no code word has weight less than d. Consider the information set consisting of the $n - d$ excluded places plus any place among the d chosen; by assigning zeroes to the $n - d$ excluded places and arbitrary elements to the last place we can generate the entire set of code words which have zeroes in all $n - d$ excluded places. There are thus q such code words, of which $q - 1$ have weight d. Since this argument obtains for an arbitrary set of d places, the total number of code words of weight d is

$$\binom{n}{d}(q - 1).$$

Similarly, let us define by $M_{d,w}$ the number of code words of weight w which are nonzero only in an arbitrary set S of w places, in a maximum code of minimum distance d. Taking as an information set the remaining $n - w$ places $\bar{S}$, plus any $w - d + 1$ of S, we generate a total of q^{w-d+1} code words with all zeroes in $\bar{S}$. Not all, however, have weight w; for every subset of S of size w' there will be $M_{d,w'}$ code words, all with all zeroes in $\bar{S}$. In addition, there is the all-zero word, so that in sum

$$\sum_{w'=d}^{w} \binom{w}{w'} M_{d,w'} = q^{w-d+1} - 1. \tag{2.1a}$$

From this recursion relation, there follows explicitly

$$M_{d,w} = (q - 1) \sum_{i=0}^{w-d} (-1)^i \binom{w-1}{i} q^{w-d-i}. \qquad (2.1b)$$

The proof is due to Kohlenberg.† Consider the linear operator $[\ ]_+$ which extracts from polynomials in positive and negative integral powers of q those terms in which q has nonnegative exponent. With the use of this operator, we rewrite Equation 2.1b as

$$M_{d,w} = (q - 1)\left[q^{-(d-1)} \sum_{i=0}^{w-1} (-1)^i \binom{w-1}{i} q^{w-1-i} \right]_+$$

$$= (q - 1)[q^{-(d-1)}(q - 1)^{w-1}]_+, \qquad (2.1c)$$

with use of the binomial expansion. For $w < d$, Equation 2.1c equals zero, so we can define $M_{d,w}$ for all w by Equation 2.1c. Parenthetically, it is clear from Equation 2.1c that, as $q \to \infty$, $M_{d,w} \to q^{w-d+1}$. Now, forming the sum on the left side of Equation 2.1a,

$$\sum_{w'=d}^{w} \binom{w}{w'} M_{d,w'} = \sum_{w'=0}^{w} \binom{w}{w'} M_{d,w'}$$

$$= (q - 1) \sum_{w'=0}^{w} \binom{w}{w'} [q^{-(d-1)}(q - 1)^{w'-1}]_+$$

$$= (q - 1)\left[q^{-(d-1)}(q - 1)^{-1} \sum_{w'=0}^{w} \binom{w}{w'}(q - 1)^{w'} \right]_+$$

$$= (q - 1)[q^{w-d+1}(q - 1)^{-1}]_+$$

$$= (q - 1)\left[\sum_{i=0}^{\infty} q^{w-d-i} \right]_+$$

$$= (q - 1) \sum_{i=0}^{w-d} q^{w-d-i}$$

$$= q^{w-d+1} - 1,$$

as was to be shown, where we have used the fact that $[\ ]_+$ is linear and the binomial expansion of $[(q - 1) + 1]^w = q^w$.

An upper bound for $M_{d,w}$ comes from the observation that, of the q^{w-d+1} code words generated by assigning elements of $GF(q)$ to any $w - d + 1$ places of S, only those in which all these $w - d + 1$

† Private communication.

symbols are nonzero have a chance of having weight w, so that

$$M_{d,w} \le (q-1)^{w-d+1}.$$

Finally, since to every set of size w there correspond $M_{d,w}$ code words, the total number $N_{d,w}$ of code words of weight w in a maximum code of length n and minimum distance d is†

$$N_{d,w} = \binom{n}{w} M_{d,w}.$$

2.3   Reed-Solomon Codes

We are now prepared to introduce Reed-Solomon[12] codes.

DEFINITION

A Reed-Solomon code on GF(q) consists of all words $\mathbf{f}$ *of length n such that the d − 1 equations*

$$\sum_{i=1}^{n} f_i Z_i^m = 0, \qquad m_0 \le m \le m_0 + d - 2, \tag{2.2}$$

are satisfied, where m_0 *and d are arbitrary integers and the* Z_i *are fixed, distinct (and when* $m_0 \ne 0$, *nonzero) elements of GF(q).*

An RS code is linear, since if $\mathbf{f}_1$ and $\mathbf{f}_2$ are words satisfying Equation 2.2, then $\beta\mathbf{f}_1 + \gamma\mathbf{f}_2$ satisfies Equation 2.2. We call Z_i the *locator* of the ith place; the length n of an RS code is limited to q or less by the condition that the locators be distinct. We shall now prove that d is the minimum distance of an RS code, by showing that any $n - d + 1$ places are an information set, whence it follows that the code is maximum.

Let us assign arbitrary elements of $GF(q)$ to an arbitrary set S of $n - d + 1$ places, and let the locators of the complementary set $\bar{S}$ be denoted by Y_j, $1 \le j \le d - 1$. We claim that the set S is an information set, and therefore that there is a unique code word corresponding to such an arbitrary assignment. The proof of this claim is that there is a unique solution to Equations 2.2 for the symbols d_j in the places corresponding to the locators Y_j. For we can write Equations 2.2 as

$$\sum_{i \in S} f_i Z_i^m + \sum_{j=1}^{d-1} d_j Y_j^m = 0, \qquad m_0 \le m \le m_0 + d - 2. \tag{2.3}$$

† It has come to my attention that independent derivations of this result are due to Kasami, Lin, and Peterson and Assmus, Gleason, and Mattson.[5]

Equations 2.3 are $d - 1$ equations in $d - 1$ unknowns; we must show they are soluble for the d_j. Define

$$S_m = - \sum_{i \in S} f_i Z_i^m ; \qquad (2.4)$$

then Equations 2.3 can be written out in matrix form as

$$\begin{bmatrix} Y_1^{m_0} & Y_2^{m_0} & \cdots & Y_{d-1}^{m_0} \\ Y_1^{m_0+1} & Y_2^{m_0+1} & \cdots & Y_{d-1}^{m_0+1} \\ \vdots & \vdots & & \vdots \\ Y_1^{m_0+d-2} & Y_2^{m_0+d-2} & \cdots & Y_{d-1}^{m_0+d-2} \end{bmatrix} \begin{bmatrix} d_1 \\ d_2 \\ \vdots \\ d_{d-1} \end{bmatrix} = \begin{bmatrix} S_{m_0} \\ S_{m_0+1} \\ \vdots \\ S_{m_0+d-2} \end{bmatrix}, \qquad (2.3a)$$

which have a solution when the coefficient matrix $\{Y_j^{m_0+i-1}\}$ has non-zero determinant. This matrix is said to be *van der Monde-like*, and has determinant

$$D = [\prod_i Y_i^{m_0}][\prod_{i>j} (Y_i - Y_j)], \qquad (2.5)$$

as can be seen by observing that $(Y_i - Y_j)$ must be a factor of the determinant for all $i \neq j$, since if $Y_i = Y_j$, $D = 0$; that $Y_i^{m_0}$ must be a factor of D for all i, since it appears in every term; that no Y_i can appear in D to a power greater than $Y_i^{m_0+d-2}$, and hence that there is no other factor of D, except possibly a constant; and that, since the coefficient of $Y_{d-1}^{m_0+d-2} Y_{d-2}^{m_0+d-3} \cdots Y_1^{m_0}$ in D must be one, this constant must be one. When $m_0 = 0$, it follows from Equation 2.5 and the fact that all Y_i are distinct that $D \neq 0$; when $m_0 \neq 0$, we have the additional condition in the definition that the Y_i be nonzero, whence $D \neq 0$. (The difference of two field elements is nonzero if they are not identical, and the product of two is nonzero if neither is zero.) This completes the proof.

From the fact that RS codes are maximum follows not only their minimum distance but also their complete weight distribution, as we saw in Section 3.2.1.

In our definition of RS codes we have required only that the locators be distinct, in order to emphasize that we may specify them in any convenient way. In the following subsection and in 2.3.3 we use this freedom to simplify implementation.

2.3.1 Cyclic RS *Codes.* A *cyclic* code is one in which, whenever **f** is a code word, any end-around cyclic shift of **f** is a code word. More precisely, if n is the length of the code and

$$\Phi_a(i) = i + a \bmod n,$$

then $\{f_{\Phi_a(i)}\}$ is a code word whenever $\{f_i\}$ is a code word. Cyclic codes permit certain types of simple instrumentation. In this section we show how by proper choice of the locators we may obtain cyclic RS codes, and we indicate the relationships between the different cyclic codes.

A few additional remarks on the properties of field elements are in order. The *order* e of a field element β is the least positive integer for which $\beta^e = 1$; that there is such an integer follows from the observation that the sequence $\beta, \beta^2, \beta^3, \cdots$ must somewhere repeat since the number of field elements is finite; but if $\beta^i = \beta^j$ then $\beta^{|i-j|} = 1$. The primitive elements are those with order $e = q - 1$. Choose one such primitive element α; the powers of α then represent the nonzero elements of the field. The order e_s of α^s must be a factor of $q - 1$, since $(\alpha^s)^{(q-1)} = 1$ for all field elements. In fact, since e_s is the smallest integer such that se_s is a multiple of $q - 1$,

$$e_s = \frac{q-1}{\mathrm{GCD}(q-1, s)}, \qquad (2.6)$$

where GCD indicates the greatest common divisor.

Let us then choose as locators Z_i the distinct nonzero field elements α^{si}, $1 \le i \le e_s$. The resulting RS code has length $n = e_s$, a factor of $q - 1$, and is cyclic. For let $\{f_i\}$ be a code word; from Equation 2.2

$$\sum_{i=1}^{e_s} f_i \alpha^{sim} = 0, \qquad m_0 \le m \le m_0 + d - 2. \qquad (2.7)$$

But then $\{f_{(i+a \bmod e_s)}\}$ is in the code; for

$$\sum_{i=1}^{e_s} f_{(i+a \bmod e_s)} \alpha^{sim} = \sum_{i'=1}^{e_s} f_{i'} \alpha^{sm(i'-a)} = \alpha^{-sma} \sum_{i'=1}^{e_s} f_{i'} \alpha^{smi'} = 0,$$

$$m_0 \le m \le m_0 + d - 2,$$

where we have changed variables and used $\alpha^{se_s} = 1$ to eliminate the "mod e_s."

We denote a particular one of these RS codes by (m_0, d, s) where $1 \le s \le q - 1$, $1 \le d \le e_s$, and $0 \le m_0 \le e_s - 1$. Clearly if $\{f_i\}$ is a code word of $(0, d, s)$, then $\{f_i \alpha^{-sm_0 i}\}$ is a code word of (m_0, d, s). If $s_0 = \mathrm{GCD}(q-1, s)$ and $b = s/s_0$, then b is less than and prime to e_s from Equation 2.6, so that the transformation

$$\Phi_b(i) = bi \bmod e_s \qquad (2.8)$$

is one-to-one and hence invertible; it follows that, if $\{f_i\}$ is a code word of (m_0, d, s_0), then $\{f_{\Phi_b^{-1}(i)}\}$ is a code word of (m_0, d, s). These relationships allow us to relate all (m_0, d, s) codes to the codes $(0, d, s_k)$, where the s_k are the divisors of $q - 1$. In particular all such codes of length $q - 1$ may be obtained from the $(0, d, 1)$ code.

As examples, let us consider the cyclic RS codes on $GF(4)$ denoted by $(0, 2, 1)$, $(0, 3, 1)$, and $(1, 3, 1)$. All have length 3. If

$$\sum_{i=1}^{3} f_i = 0,$$

$\{f_i\}$ is an element of $(0, 2, 1)$; to generate the code, we can take f_1 and f_2 as information symbols, and use

$$f_3 = f_2 + f_1$$

(omitting minus signs in this field of characteristic two). Using Table 2.5, we find the code words to be

$$
\begin{array}{llll}
000 & 101 & \alpha 0\alpha & \alpha^2 0\alpha^2 \\
011 & 110 & \alpha 1\alpha^2 & \alpha^2 1\alpha \\
0\alpha\alpha & 1\alpha\alpha^2 & \alpha\alpha 0 & \alpha^2\alpha 1 \\
0\alpha^2\alpha^2 & 1\alpha^2\alpha & \alpha\alpha^2 1 & \alpha^2\alpha^2 0
\end{array}
\tag{2.9a}
$$

Similarly, for $(0, 3, 1)$ we can solve the equations

$$f_1 + f_2 + f_3 = 0$$
$$f_1\alpha + f_2\alpha^2 + f_3 = 0$$

to obtain $f_2 = f_1\alpha$, $f_3 = f_1\alpha^2$, and thence the code words

$$000 \qquad 1\alpha\alpha^2 \qquad \alpha\alpha^2 1 \qquad \alpha^2 1\alpha. \tag{2.9b}$$

Finally, from $(0, 3, 1)$ we can obtain $(1, 3, 1)$ by the relationship $g_i = f_i\alpha^{-1}$:

$$000 \qquad \alpha^2\alpha^2\alpha^2 \qquad 111 \qquad \alpha\alpha\alpha. \tag{2.9c}$$

There is one other type of code closely related to the cyclic codes which should be mentioned; we call it *cyclic-plus*, and denote it $(+, d, s)$. It is the code obtained by letting $m_0 = 0$ and using in addition to the locators α^{si}, $1 \le i \le e_s$, the locator $Z_0 = 0$. With the convention $0^0 = 1$, we then have from Equation 2.2 that $\{f_i\}$ is in the code if

$$f_0 + \sum_{i=1}^{e_s} f_i = 0$$

$$\sum_{i=1}^{e_s} f_i\alpha^{sim} = 0, \qquad 1 \le m \le d - 2. \tag{2.10}$$

Therefore $(+, d, s)$ is obtained from $(1, d - 1, s)$ by adjoining an overall parity check

$$f_0 = -\sum_{i=1}^{e_s} f_i;$$

it has the same number of words, length greater by one, and a minimum distance greater by one.

Certain types of decoding[6] depend upon finding permutations, like the cyclic permutation, which leave the code invariant. There is an interesting such permutation for the cyclic-plus RS codes of length q, all of which can be derived from the $(+, d, 1)$ code by the permutation of Equation 2.8. Let us for the moment adopt the convention that $\alpha^0 = 0$, while $\alpha^{q-1} = 1$; then Equation 2.10 can be written

$$\sum_{i=0}^{q-1} f_i(\alpha^i)^m = 0, \qquad 0 \le m \le d - 2. \tag{2.10a}$$

Then let $\Phi_+(i)$ be the permutation such that

$$\alpha^{\Phi_+(i)} = \alpha^i + 1, \qquad 0 \le i \le q - 1. \tag{2.11}$$

The permutation $\Phi_+^t(i)$ obtained by applying $\Phi_+(i)$ t times is specified by

$$\alpha^{\Phi_+^{t}(i)} = \alpha^i + t(1),$$

so that if p is the characteristic of the field, $\Phi_+^p(i)$ is the identity permutation, and $\Phi_+(i)$ has the inverse $\Phi_+^{p-1}(i)$. (We see that $\Phi_+(i)$ involves q/p cyclic permutations of sets of size p.) Now if $\{f_i\}$ is a code word in $(+, d, 1)$, then $\{f_{\Phi_+^{-1}(i)}\}$ is a code word, since

$$\sum_{i=0}^{q-1} f_{\Phi_+^{-1}(i)}(\alpha^i)^m = \sum_{i=0}^{q-1} f_i[\alpha^{\Phi_+(i)}]^m$$

$$= \sum_{i=0}^{q-1} f_i(\alpha^i + 1)^m$$

$$= \sum_{j=0}^{m} \binom{m}{j} \sum_{i=0}^{q-1} f_i \alpha^{ji} = 0, \qquad 0 \le m \le d - 2,$$

where we have applied the permutation $\Phi_+(i)$, substituted Equation 2.11, used the binomial theorem, and observed that $0 \le j \le m \le d - 2$, so that we can substitute Equation 2.2. From $\Phi_+(i)$ and the cyclic permutation, we can obtain[4] any of the $q(q - 1)$ permutations $\Phi_{\beta_1 \beta_2}(i)$ for which

$$\alpha^{\Phi_{\beta_1 \beta_2}(i)} = \beta_1 \alpha^i + \beta_2,$$

where β_1 and β_2 are arbitrary elements of $GF(q)$, except that $\beta_1 \ne 0$. Thus we have discovered a relatively large group of permutations (the doubly transitive affine group) under which cyclic-plus codes of length q are invariant.†

---

† This result has also been obtained by Kasami, Lin, and Peterson.[5]

2.3.2   Encoding and Decoding RS *Codes.* That RS codes have the greatest minimum distance possible for any given rate makes us desire to use them; that their structure permits relatively simple implementation allows us to do so.

Encoding is simplest when the RS code is cyclic or cyclic-plus. Peterson[9] has given a general circuit for encoding cyclic codes, which consists of a shift register with feedback. In Figure 2.1 we have added

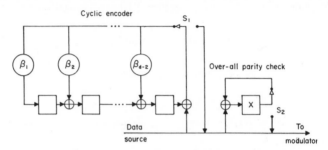

Figure 2.1   Encoder for a cyclic-plus code. □, element that stores an element of $GF(q)$; ⊕, $GF(q)$ adder; β_i, multiplier by β_i in $GF(q)$.

an over-all parity check to this configuration to give some idea how a cyclic-plus code might be encoded. The β_i, $1 \le i \le d - 2$, are elements of $GF(q)$ whose values depend on the details of the code; for the principles of this encoder the reader is referred to Peterson.

The encoder has $d - 1$ $GF(q)$ storage elements; if $q = 2^m$, as will normally be the case, then the elements of $GF(q)$ can be represented by binary vectors of length m, and each storage element can be realized by m flip-flops. Adding in $GF(2^m)$ can be done by m parallel additions in $GF(2)$, as we saw in Section 2.1, and is realized by flipping the flip-flops. Multiplication by a fixed element β_i of $GF(q)$ can be accomplished by an m-input, m-output combinational network, or by m shifts of an m-bit accumulator with feedback.[10]

The operation of the encoder is as follows. With switch S_1 set for feedback, $n - d + 1$ information symbols are shifted into the encoder and simultaneously fed to the modulator. Then switch S_1 is turned to disable the feedback and shift the $d - 2$ check symbols in the shift register to the modulator, clearing the shift register. Meanwhile storage register X has been accumulating the sum of all information and check symbols; on the nth symbol only, S_2 is switched to empty its contents into the modulator.

Decoding involves altogether a different order of complexity. Whereas an RS encoder is realized by a piece of digital circuitry, an RS decoder is essentially a programmed general-purpose digital computer with a

GF(*q*) arithmetic unit—that is, with the capability of being instructed to add, multiply, and divide elements of *GF*(*q*). Lest the reader be appalled by the term "general-purpose," we hasten to add that such a computer need not be a giant, nor terribly fast; the general-purpose structure is required only in order that an algorithm of several steps be executable, and the speed need only be fast enough to keep up with the data.†

In Appendix B we discuss in detail decoding algorithms for RS codes, and analyze closely the number of operations required to carry them out. Our major results, both new, are that a *GF*(*q*) computer can correct:

1. Any combination of *s* erasures such that $s < d$, in a number of operations (principally multiplications) proportional to s^2;

2. Any combination of *t* errors and *s* erasures such that $2t + s < d$, in a number of operations proportional to t^3.

The complexity of an operation itself increases no more rapidly than m^2, where $q = 2^m$. The memory required is no greater than d^2 registers, where each register has length *m*. In sum, the complexity of a Reed-Solomon decoder is proportional to m^2d^3 at the worst. Even without inquiring closely into the constant of proportionality, we can infer that the complexity of the decoder for a long and powerful RS code is not going to be impossibly greater than that for a shorter, simpler one.‡

2.3.3 Shortened RS Codes. Sometimes it happens that we have an inner code which is very long, but want to use as an outer code an RS code of only moderate length. That is, if $q = e^{NR}$ is the number of inner code words and *n* is the desired length of the RS code, $n \ll q$. In this case, if it happens that *GF*(*q*) has a subfield *GF*(*q'*) such that $q' \geq n$, we can simplify implementation of the RS code by choosing locators from *GF*(*q'*).

In Section 2.1 we asserted that an element of $GF(p^m)$ could be represented as a vector of *m* elements of *GF*(*p*). Here we further assert that if *GF*(*q'*) is a subfield of *GF*(*q*), so that $q = q'^b$ for some *b*, then an element *β* of *GF*(*q*) can be represented as a vector of *b* elements from *GF*(*q'*):

$$\beta = (\beta_1, \beta_2, \cdots, \beta_b), \qquad \beta_j \in GF(q'), \qquad 1 \leq j \leq b.$$

† In a detailed study, Zierler[15] determined that a small general-purpose machine costing about \$30,000 and with 1 microsecond cycle time could be programmed to decode a Reed-Solomon code on *GF*(256) correcting several tens of errors, at a data rate of 2400 bits per second.

‡ Berlekamp has just announced a still more efficient decoding algorithm, for which the number of operations in a general-purpose computer grows only as the square of *t*.

Furthermore, addition of two elements β and γ of $GF(q)$ can be carried out place-by-place according to the rules of addition in $GF(q')$:

$$\beta + \gamma = (\beta_1 + \gamma_1, \beta_2 + \gamma_2, \cdots, \beta_b + \gamma_b);$$

and multiplication of β by some element β' of $GF(q')$ can be carried out place-by-place in $GF(q')$:

$$\beta'\beta = (\beta'\beta_1, \beta'\beta_2, \cdots, \beta'\beta_b).$$

Suppose, then, that we choose the locators Z_i of an RS code on $GF(q)$ to be distinct elements of $GF(q')$. All the powers of Z_i are then also members of $GF(q')$. If we represent the elements f_i of a code word $\mathbf{f}$ by b elements of $GF(q')$, we find that $\mathbf{f}$ is a code word if

$$\sum_i f_i Z_i^m = \sum_i (f_{i1}Z_i^m, f_{i2}Z_i^m, \cdots, f_{ib}Z_i^m) = (0, 0, \cdots, 0),$$

$$m_0 \le m \le m_0 + d - 2,$$

so that we must have separately for each place

$$\sum_i f_{ij}Z_i^m = 0, \qquad m_0 \le m \le m_0 + d - 2, \qquad 1 \le j \le b.$$

We see that we have created our RS code on $GF(q)$ out of b interlaced RS codes of the same m_0 and d on $GF(q')$. Since $GF(q')$ is a much smaller field than $GF(q)$, encoding and decoding will generally be markedly simplified. The correction power of the RS code cannot be decreased by this choice of locators and in fact may be increased whenever it happens that, when there is an error in a symbol from $GF(q)$, there are errors in only a few constituent elements from $GF(q')$.

2.3.4   Another Treatment of RS *Codes.* In this subsection we present briefly another treatment of RS codes. Though not original with us, this treatment is sufficiently provocative in its elegance and simplicity that we feel it deserves wider circulation. It is in fact the original treatment of Reed and Solomon[12] with features from Mattson and Solomon.[7]

Let F_j, $0 \le j \le n - d$, be $n - d + 1$ arbitrary symbols from $GF(q)$, with $n = q - 1$. Define the polynomial $F(x)$ by

$$F(x) = \sum_{j=0}^{n-d} F_j x^j.$$

The elements f_i of the code word $\mathbf{f}$ corresponding to these symbols are then defined to be

$$f_i = F(\alpha^i) = \sum_{j=0}^{n-d} F_j \alpha^{ij}, \qquad 0 \le i \le n - 1, \qquad (2.12)$$

where α is some primitive element of $GF(q)$. Observe that, unless all the F_j are zeroes, $F(x)$ is a polynomial of degree less than or equal to $n - d$ and by the fundamental theorem of algebra can have no more than $n - d$ roots. Therefore as α^i takes on the values of the n nonzero elements of the field, at least d of the f_i must be nonzero. It follows that the minimum weight of any nonzero code word is d.

The f_i and F_j are in a sense transforms of one another, like Fourier transforms. On $GF(q)$, the basic transform relation is the following:

$$\sum_{i=0}^{n-1} \alpha^{(j-j')i} = -\delta_{jj'}, \tag{2.13}$$

where δ is the Kronecker delta, since

$$\sum_{i=0}^{n-1} \alpha^{(j-j')i} = n = -1 \bmod p, \qquad j = j';$$

$$\sum_{i=0}^{n-1} \alpha^{(j-j')i} = \frac{\alpha^{(j-j')n} - 1}{\alpha^{(j-j')} - 1} = 0, \qquad j \neq j',$$

where we have used $n = p^m - 1$ and $\beta^n = 1$. If we then define the polynomial $f(x)$ by

$$f(x) = \sum_{i=0}^{n-1} f_i x^i,$$

we find by substitution of Equations 2.12 and 2.13 that

$$-f(\alpha^{-j}) = -\sum_{i=0}^{n-1} f_i \alpha^{-ij} = \sum_{j'=0}^{n-d} F_{j'} \sum_{i=0}^{n-1} \alpha^{i(j'-j)}$$

$$= \begin{cases} F_j, & 0 \le j \le n - d; \\ 0, & n - d + 1 \le j \le n - 1. \end{cases}$$

Since $\alpha^{-(n-m)} = \alpha^m$,

$$f(\alpha^m) = \sum_{i=0}^{n-1} f_i \alpha^{im} = 0, \qquad 1 \le m \le d - 1,$$

so that this is the $(1, d, 1)$ cyclic RS code described earlier from which all other cyclic RS codes of length n can be derived. In this sense, an RS code consists of all $\{f_i\}$ whose transforms are zero over a certain continuous range.

2.4 BCH Codes

Use of a Reed-Solomon code is always indicated when a code on $GF(q)$ of length $n \le q$ and of any minimum distance is required, since

RS codes are maximum. But often the required n exceeds q; for instance, if the code must be binary, the longest RS code has length 2. The BCH codes[2] are a satisfactory solution to the problem of finding a code on $GF(q)$ of length n and minimum distance d when n is not extravagantly large.

Let b be some integer such that $q^b \geq n$. Then there is an RS code on $GF(q^b)$ of length n and minimum distance d. Since $GF(q)$ is a subfield of $GF(q^b)$, there is a certain subset of code words from this code all of whose symbols are in $GF(q)$. The minimum distance between any two words in this subset is not less than d; therefore, this subset can be taken as a code on $GF(q)$ of length n and minimum distance at least d. Any such subset we call a BCH *code*; $GF(q)$ is called the *symbol field* and $GF(q^b)$ the *locator field* of the code.

Since the sum or product of two elements from $GF(q)$ is in $GF(q)$, $\beta \mathbf{f_1} + \gamma \mathbf{f_2}$ is in a BCH code if $\mathbf{f_1}$ and $\mathbf{f_2}$ are code words and β and γ are elements of $GF(q)$. Therefore a BCH code is linear and must have q^k words, where the number of information symbols k has yet to be determined; how useful the code is depends on how large k is. If the parent RS code is cyclic or cyclic-plus, then the derived BCH code is cyclic or cyclic-plus.

For example, from the $(0, 2, 1)$, $(0, 3, 1)$, and $(1, 3, 1)$ cyclic RS codes on $GF(4)$ which were written out in Equations 2.9a, 2.9b, and 2.9c of Section 2.3.1, we can derive the three binary BCH codes:

(a) 000   (b) 000   (c) 000
     011   111
     101
     110

From the fact that the three codes have respectively 2, 0, and 1 information symbols, we see that k depends in general on both m_0 and d, and that it may even be zero.

We now determine the number of information symbols in a BCH code on $GF(q)$ derived from an (m_0, d, s) cyclic RS code on $GF(q^b)$. We recall from Section 2.3.1 that such an RS code has locators $Z_i = \alpha^{is}$, $1 \leq i \leq n$, where α is a primitive element of $GF(q^b)$ and the length n is the order e_s of α^s; the code consists of all words $\{f_i\}$ satisfying

$$0 = \sum_{i=1}^{e_s} f_i Z_i^m, \qquad m_0 \leq m \leq m_0 + d - 2. \qquad (2.14a)$$

The derived BCH code consists of all words $\{f_i\}$ with elements from $GF(q)$ satisfying Equation 2.14a.

We know that $GF(q)$ and $GF(q^b)$ are fields with the same characteristic, since if $q = p^m$, $q^b = p^{bm}$. In $GF(q^b)$ raising to the pth power any number of times is a linear operation, from Section 2.1; in particular, since $q = p^m$, raising to the qth power is linear. Raising Equations 2.14a to the qth power, we obtain

$$0 = \left(\sum_i f_i Z_i^m\right)^q = \sum_i f_i^q Z_i^{mq} = \sum_i f_i Z_i^{mq}, \qquad m_0 \le m \le m_0 + d - 2,$$

$$(2.14b)$$

where we have used the fact that $f_i^q = f_i$ since $f_i \in GF(q)$. Equations 2.14b are in general a new set of equations of the same form as 2.14a satisfied by the BCH code words. Furthermore, by repeatedly raising Equation 2.14a to the qth power, we find that $\{f_i\}$ satisfies all the equations

$$0 = \sum_{i=1}^{e_s} f_i Z_i^{mq^j}, \qquad m_0 \le m \le m_0 + d - 2, \qquad 0 \le j \le b - 1$$

$$(2.14c)$$

where the process terminates at $j = b - 1$ since $Z_i^{mq^b} = Z_i^m$, $Z_i \in GF(q^b)$.

Not all these equations are actually different. If

$$mq^j = m'q^{j'} \bmod e_s, \qquad m \ne m', \qquad j \ne j',$$

then

$$Z_i^{mq^j} = \alpha^{ismq^j} = \alpha^{ism'q^{j'}} = Z_i^{m'q^{j'}}, \qquad 1 \le i \le e_s,$$

since $\alpha^{se_s} = 1$. Let us denote by r the number of equations which are distinct—that is, the number of distinct integers modulo e_s in the set

$$m_0, qm_0, \cdots, q^{b-1}m_0$$

$$m_0 + 1, q(m_0 + 1), \cdots, q^{b-1}(m_0 + 1) \qquad (2.15)$$

$$\cdot \quad \cdot \quad \cdot \quad \cdot \quad \cdot \quad \cdot \quad \cdot \quad \cdot \quad \cdot \quad \cdot \quad \cdot \quad \cdot \quad \cdot \quad \cdot \quad \cdot \quad \cdot \quad \cdot$$

$$m_0 + d - 2, q(m_0 + d - 2), \cdots, q^{b-1}(m_0 + d - 2)$$

Clearly $r \le b(d - 1)$. We label the distinct members of the set 2.15 as m_l, $1 \le l \le r$; then the BCH words $\{f_i\}$ satisfy

$$0 = \sum_i f_i Z_i^{m_l}, \qquad 1 \le l \le r. \qquad (2.14d)$$

We now show that r is the number of check symbols in the BCH code. Let β be any element of $GF(q^b)$ with r consecutive powers $(\beta^{a+1}, \beta^{a+2}, \cdots, \beta^{a+r})$ among the code locators. In particular α^s is such an element. We claim that the places whose locators are the r consecutive powers of β may be taken as a check set, and the remaining $n - r$ as an information set S. To prove this claim, we assign arbitrary elements of $GF(q)$ to f_i, $i \in S$; then from Equations 2.14d

$$0 = \sum_{i \in S} f_i Z_i^{m_l} + \sum_{l'=1}^{r} d_{l'} \beta^{(a+l')m_l}, \qquad 1 \le l \le r, \qquad (2.14e)$$

where we have defined $d_{l'}$ to be the unknown symbol corresponding to the locator $\beta^{(a+l')}$. Further defining

$$S_l = - \sum_{i \in S} f_i Z_i^{m_l},$$

we write Equations 2.14e in matrix form as

$$\begin{bmatrix} \beta^{(a+1)m_1} & \beta^{(a+2)m_1} & \cdots & \beta^{(a+r)m_1} \\ \beta^{(a+1)m_2} & \beta^{(a+2)m_2} & \cdots & \beta^{(a+r)m_2} \\ \vdots & \vdots & & \vdots \\ \beta^{(a+1)m_r} & \beta^{(a+2)m_r} & \cdots & \beta^{(a+r)m_r} \end{bmatrix} \begin{bmatrix} d_1 \\ d_2 \\ \vdots \\ d_r \end{bmatrix} = \begin{bmatrix} S_1 \\ S_2 \\ \vdots \\ S_r \end{bmatrix} \qquad (2.14f)$$

In Equations 2.14f the coefficient matrix $\{\beta^{m_l(a+l')}\}$ is van der Mondelike and, since the β^{m_l} are distinct and nonzero, it has nonzero determinant. Therefore it can be inverted to give a solution for the $d_{l'}$, so that S is an information set as claimed.

It remains to show that the $d_{l'}$ which solve Equations 2.14f and hence 2.14d are elements of $GF(q)$, so that the word obtained is in the BCH code. Raising Equations 2.14d to the qth power, we obtain

$$\sum_i f_i^q Z_i^{qm_l} = 0, \qquad 1 \le l \le r. \qquad (2.14g)$$

But for $i \in S$, $f_i \in GF(q)$, so $f_i^q = f_i$. Furthermore, Equations 2.14g are precisely the same equations as 2.14d, since multiplying each element in the set 2.15 by q and reducing modulo e_s leaves the set unchanged. Thus $d_{l'}^q$ solve Equations 2.14d for the same information symbols f_i as $d_{l'}$; but this solution is unique, so that $d_{l'}^q = d_{l'}$ and $d_{l'} \in GF(q)$.

The derived BCH code has therefore an information set of $n - r$ symbols, and q^{n-r} code words.

We remark that a lower bound to the number of information sets of a BCH code can be obtained from the fact, just proved, that every set of r places whose locators can be represented as r consecutive powers of some locator field element is a check set.

As an example, to find the number of check symbols in the binary code of length 15 and minimum distance 7 derived from the (1, 7, 1) RS code, we write the set 2.15 as

1	2	4	8
2	4	8	1
3	6	12	9
4	8	1	2
5	10	5	10
6	12	9	3

where we have reduced all integers modulo 15. One rapidly learns to write only the unduplicated integers:

1	2	4	8
3	6	12	9
5	10.		

It follows that r, the number of check symbols, is 10; this is the (15, 5) binary Bose-Chaudhuri code. Peterson[8] tabulates $n - r$ for a large range of binary BCH codes.

The cyclic-plus BCH code derived from the $(+, d, s)$ RS code has both length and minimum distance greater by one than the cyclic BCH code derived from the $(1, d - 1, s)$ RS code, and has the same number of information symbols.

As the BCH code words are also words in the parent RS code, they can always be decoded by the algorithms of Appendix B. The only modification is that if the decoding algorithm yields a word not a member of the BCH code—that is, a word with symbols not all in the symbol field—an uncorrectable error is detected. There has been some success in finding digital circuitry capable of decoding some binary BCH codes, in preference to using a decoder with general-purpose computer structure.

We might mention that from our remark under Equation 2.15 the number of check symbols r needed to give a minimum distance d is guaranteed to be less than $b(d - 1)$; but b must increase with n at least as $\log_q n$, since $n \le q^b$, so to the accuracy of this bound for very large n either $d/n \to 0$ or $r \to n$. It was in this sense that we remarked in Chapter 1 that BCH codes were asymptotically useless. It is well to point out, however, that cases are known[7] in which the minimum distance of the BCH code is considerably larger than that of the RS code from which it was derived, and that it is suspected (so far without proof) that at least for certain codes asymptotic performance is not nearly as bad as this result would indicate.

References

1. E. Artin, *Galois Theory*, Edwards Bros. Inc., Ann Arbor, Michigan, 1944.
2. R. C. Bose and D. K. Ray-Chaudhuri, "On a Class of Error-Correcting Binary Group Codes," and "Further Results on Error-Correcting Binary Group Codes," *Information and Control*, **3**, 68–79 and 279–290 (1960); A. Hocquenghem, "Codes Correcteurs d'Erreurs," *Chiffres*, **2**, 147–156 (1959); see also Peterson, *op. cit.*, Chapter 9.
3. R. D. Carmichael, *Introduction to the Theory of Groups of Finite Order*, Ginn & Company, Boston, Massachusetts, 1937; also Dover Publications, New York, 1956.
4. *Ibid.*, Section 67.
5. T. Kasami, S. Lin, and W. W. Peterson, "Some Results on Weight Distributions of BCH Codes," *IEEE Trans. Information Theory* (Los Angeles Symposium), **IT-12**, 274 (1966); E. F. Assmus, Jr., A. M. Gleason, and H. F. Mattson, Sylvania Summary Scientific Report No. 4, Contract AF19(604)–8516, AFCRL, Bedford, Massachusetts, 1965.
6. J. MacWilliams, "Permutation Decoding of Systematic Codes," *Bell System Tech. J.*, **43**, 485–506 (1964).
7. H. F. Mattson and G. Solomon, "A New Treatment of Bose-Chaudhuri Codes," *J. Soc. Indust. Appl. Math.*, **9**, 654–669 (1961).
8. W. W. Peterson, *Error Correcting Codes*, M.I.T. Press and John Wiley & Sons, Inc., New York, 1961.
9. *Ibid.*, Section 8.5.
10. *Ibid.*, Section 7.3; T. C. Bartee and D. I. Schneider, "Computation with Finite Fields," *Information and Control*, **6**, 79–98 (1963).
11. E. Prange, "The Use of Information Sets in Decoding Cyclic Codes," *IRE Trans. Information Theory* (Brussels Symposium), **IT-8**, s5–s9 (1962).
12. I. S. Reed and G. Solomon, "Polynomial Codes over Certain Finite Fields," *J. Soc. Indust. Appl. Math.*, **8**, 300–314 (1960); also see Peterson, *op. cit.*, Section 9.3.
13. R. C. Singleton, "Maximum Distance *q*–Nary Codes," *IEEE Trans. Information Theory*, **IT-10**, 116–118 (1964).
14. D. Slepian, "A Class of Binary Signaling Alphabets," *Bell System Tech. J.*, **35**, 203–234 (1956).
15. N. Zierler, Private Communication.

3. Generalized Minimum Distance Decoding

The purpose of this chapter is to introduce a distance measure, called generalized distance, which allows us to use likelihood information in algebraic decoding algorithms. Our development shows that these ideas involve generalizations of the familiar concepts of Hamming distance, erasures, and minimum distance decoding, the basic results about which we present in a general framework; we also discuss the relationship between GMD and likelihood decoding. We develop bounds on the performance obtainable with GMD decoding, which enable us to show the improvement over strictly algebraic decoding; in one case, this performance is effectively as good as that obtainable with maximum likelihood decoding.

We discuss first the binary case, which lends itself to a geometrical exposition; we then discuss the nonbinary case, in which the results are almost identical.

3.1 Decoding Binary Signals

We recall our schematic description of Chapter 1 of a communications system as seen by a particular encoder-decoder pair. The encoder receives one of e^{NR} commands m, $1 \leq m \leq e^{NR}$, from a data source and generates an input sequence $\mathbf{x}_m$ of length N (a code word) for the modulator. In this section we shall assume that this sequence is binary—that

35

is, that each element may be one of only two symbols, which we label 0 and 1 to make them correspond to elements of $GF(2)$. The modulator generates for each symbol the corresponding one of two signals, which is sent over a memoryless channel and demodulated into some output y. A detector processes y and puts out an information packet which in the binary case turns out always to be a real-valued scalar, which we call a *weight* and label α. Finally, the decoder accepts a sequence $\boldsymbol{\alpha}$ of N weights, called a *received word*, and from them produces an estimate $\hat{m}$ of which of the e^{NR} code words was sent. Figure 3.1 recapitulates this description.

Figure 3.1   Transmission chain.

We have seen in Section 1.3 that we may always include a likelihood detector after y without destroying information. In the binary case the output of this likelihood detector may be taken to be the *bit log likelihood ratio*

$$L(y) = \ln \frac{\Pr(y \mid 1)}{\Pr(y \mid 0)}, \tag{3.1}$$

rather than the pair of likelihoods $\Pr(y \mid 1)$ and $\Pr(y \mid 0)$, as we shall shortly see when we discuss maximum likelihood decoding. We shall find that all the detectors we consider consist of a likelihood detector followed by a quantizer with characteristic $q(x)$, so that

$$\alpha(y) = q[L(y)]. \tag{3.2}$$

As is suggested by our notation, it is illuminating to consider the sequence $\boldsymbol{\alpha}$ of N weights as a vector or point in N space, of which the α_i, $1 \le i \le N$, are coordinates. Define

$$s(x) = \begin{cases} -1, & x = 0 \\ +1, & x = 1 \end{cases}; \tag{3.3}$$

then we can identify the input sequence

$$\mathbf{x}_m = (x_{m1}, x_{m2}, \cdots, x_{mN})$$

with the point in N space

$$\mathbf{x}_m = (s(x_{m1}), s(x_{m2}), \cdots, s(x_{mN})),$$

where the use of the same symbol $\mathbf{x}_m$ for $GF(2)$ sequence and real point should not cause confusion. We shall find that all the decoding criteria we consider—maximum likelihood, Hamming distance, generalized minimum distance—can be formulated in terms of minimizing the Euclidean distance d_E between $\boldsymbol{\alpha}$ and the code word $\mathbf{x}_m$, where

$$d_E^2(\boldsymbol{\alpha}, \mathbf{x}_m) = |\boldsymbol{\alpha} - \mathbf{x}_m|^2 = |\boldsymbol{\alpha}|^2 - 2\boldsymbol{\alpha} \cdot \mathbf{x}_m + |\mathbf{x}_m|^2. \qquad (3.4)$$

For a given $\boldsymbol{\alpha}$, minimizing $d_E(\boldsymbol{\alpha}, \mathbf{x}_m)$ over m is equivalent to maximizing the dot product $\boldsymbol{\alpha} \cdot \mathbf{x}_m$, since $|\boldsymbol{\alpha}|^2$ is a constant and $|\mathbf{x}_m|^2 = N$ for all m, from Equation 3.3; while minimizing the Euclidean distance is simpler to visualize, maximizing the dot product is easier to analyze.

Finally, we observe that in general minimizing $d_E(\boldsymbol{\alpha}, \mathbf{x}_m)$ over m involves computing the distance between the received word and each of the e^{NR} code words. We shall find that, when the code words are from a code of minimum distance d, there can be at most one code word $\mathbf{x}_m$ such that a condition of the form

$$f(\boldsymbol{\alpha} \cdot \mathbf{x}_m) > D_0$$

holds for any $\boldsymbol{\alpha}$, and that if this condition is satisfied $\mathbf{x}_m$ is the closest code word to $\boldsymbol{\alpha}$. Thus if we have an expeditious way of finding this $\mathbf{x}_m$, we can avoid the e^{NR} comparisons otherwise necessary. On the other hand, no such $\mathbf{x}_m$ may exist for some $\boldsymbol{\alpha}$; in this case, a decoder which depends on the condition being satisfied will fail to decode. For lack of better terminology, we shall call the latter type of decoding *conditional*, and the former *exhaustive*. A particular decoder will then be specified by one of these terms and the distance measure used.

Figure 3.2 illustrates the general framework for the detector and

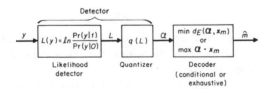

Figure 3.2 General detector-decoder framework.

decoder within which we have claimed we will always be able to work.

3.1.1 Maximum Likelihood Decoding. A maximum likelihood decoder chooses that $\hat{m}$ for which $\ln \Pr(\mathbf{y} \mid \mathbf{x}_m)$ is maximum. Under the assumption of equiprobable $\mathbf{x}_m$, it is the optimum decoder in the sense of minimizing the probability of error ($\hat{m} \neq m$). If the channel is memoryless,

$$\ln \Pr(\mathbf{y} \mid \mathbf{x}_m) = \sum_{i=1}^{N} \ln \Pr(y_i \mid x_{mi}). \tag{3.5}$$

If

$$\ln \Pr(\mathbf{y} \mid \mathbf{x}_m) > \ln \Pr(\mathbf{y} \mid \mathbf{x}_{m'})$$

and

$$x_{mi} \neq x_{m'i}, \qquad i \in S;$$

$$x_{mi} = x_{m'i}, \qquad i \notin S,$$

then by substitution of Equation 3.5

$$\sum_{i \in S} \ln \Pr(y_i \mid x_{mi}) > \sum_{i \in S} \ln \Pr(y_i \mid x_{m'i}),$$

or

$$\sum_{i \in S} \ln \frac{\Pr(y_i \mid x_{mi})}{\Pr(y_i \mid x_{m'i})} > 0,$$

or

$$\sum_{i \in S} s(x_{mi}) L_i > 0,$$

where we have substituted Equations 3.1 and 3.3 and used $x_{mi} \neq x_{m'i}$, $i \in S$. It follows that the $\hat{m}$ which maximizes Equation 3.5 also maximizes

$$\sum_{i=1}^{N} s(x_{mi}) L_i = \mathbf{x}_m \cdot \mathbf{L}, \tag{3.6}$$

or equivalently minimizes the Euclidean distance $d_E(\mathbf{L}, \mathbf{x}_m)$. If we then choose a linear quantizer with characteristic

$$q(x) = Kx,$$

so that

$$\boldsymbol{\alpha} = K\mathbf{L},$$

where K is any constant scale factor, we justify our claim that maximum likelihood decoding can be done within the framework of Figure 3.2. It is necessarily exhaustive.

The set of $\mathbf{L}$ for which m is the output of the decoder is called the *decision region* R_m. In this case

$$\mathbf{L} \in R_m \quad \text{if} \quad \mathbf{L} \cdot \mathbf{x}_m > \mathbf{L} \cdot \mathbf{x}_{m'}, \qquad \text{all } m' \neq m.$$

On the decision boundary between R_m and $R_{m'}$, $\mathbf{L}$ satisfies

$$\mathbf{L} \cdot \mathbf{x}_m = \mathbf{L} \cdot \mathbf{x}_{m'}$$

or

$$\mathbf{L} \cdot (\mathbf{x}_m - \mathbf{x}_{m'}) = 0.$$

The boundary is therefore part of an $(N - 1)$-dimensional hyperplane which passes through the origin, and a decision region is a hyperpyramid with vertex at the origin.

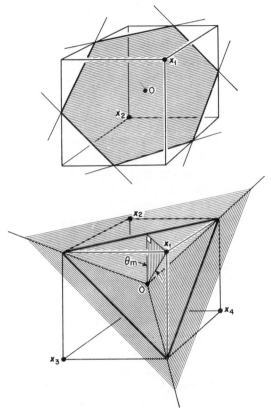

Figure 3.3   Geometric representation of (3, 1) and (3, 2) codes with decision regions for x_1.

A decoding scheme of the conditional type could be based on the following observation. Let R'_m be the largest hypercone centered on x_m with vertex at the origin which can be included entirely in the hyperpyramid R_m; it is defined by an angle θ_m such that if

$$\cos \theta(x_m, L) = \frac{x_m \cdot L}{\sqrt{N|L|^2}} > \cos \theta_m, \tag{3.7a}$$

then L is in R'_m. For a binary linear code with minimum distance D,

$$\cos \theta_m = \sqrt{1 - \frac{D}{N}}, \tag{3.7b}$$

which can be seen by observing that, if $\mathbf{x}_{m'}$ is distance D from $\mathbf{x}_m$, and if $x_{m'i} \neq x_{mi}$, $i \in S$, then the point $\mathbf{z}$ with coordinates

$$z_i = \begin{cases} s(x_{mi}), & i \notin S; \\ 0, & i \in S, \end{cases}$$

is the closest point on the decision boundary to $\mathbf{x}_m$, since $(\mathbf{x}_m - \mathbf{z})$ is perpendicular to the boundary hyperplane; further, that $\mathbf{z}$ is on the cone boundary as well, and with $\mathbf{x}_m$ and the origin forms a right triangle whose angle at the origin is θ_m.

Figure 3.3 illustrates these geometrical concepts with the (3, 1) and (3, 2) codes, which have minimum distances 3 and 2.

In general, in order to determine in which decision region $\mathbf{L}$ lies, the decoder must calculate all dot products $\mathbf{L} \cdot \mathbf{x}_m$, $1 \leq n \leq e^{NR}$. However, if it finds some $\mathbf{x}_m$ such that Equation 3.7a is satisfied, it may terminate its search, without computing any more dot products. Unfortunately, even when $\mathbf{L}$ is such that Equation 3.7a is satisfied for some $\mathbf{x}_m$, no methods are known for rapidly discovering this $\mathbf{x}_m$. The great advantage of the minimum distance techniques now to be discussed, which are based on similar principles, is that we can give decoding algorithms which find the "closest" $\mathbf{x}_m$—in terms, however, of a nonoptimum distance measure.

3.1.2 Hamming Distance Decoding. For algebraic decoding algorithms one generally assumes a hard decision made by the detector, so that its output can be considered an element of the same field as the input. In the binary case, one uses a detector which puts out 0 if $\Pr(y \mid 0)$ is greater than $\Pr(y \mid 1)$, and vice versa. In terms of our formulation, such a detector consists of a likelihood detector followed by a two-valued quantizer with characteristic

$$q(L) = \begin{cases} +1, & L \geq 0; \\ -1, & L < 0. \end{cases}$$

Therefore the point $\boldsymbol{\alpha}$ can be located only on vertices of the same hypercube on whose vertices the code points are located; the received words have the same character as the code words. Figure 3.4 illustrates the possible received words for a code of length 3.

The Hamming distance between two code words $\mathbf{x}_m$ and $\mathbf{x}_{m'}$ is defined, we recall, as the number of places $d_{mm'}$ in which the words differ; their dot product is equal to

$$\mathbf{x}_m \cdot \mathbf{x}_{m'} = n - 2d_{mm'},$$

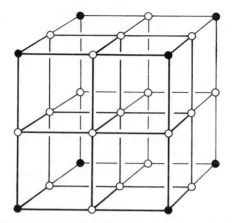

Figure 3.4 Possible received words of length 3. ●, possible received words with errors-only decoding; ○, possible received words with erasures-and-errors decoding; —, entire cube interior possible with GMD decoding.

where n is the length of the code. Since with a hard decision quantizer a received word α has the same character as a code word, the Hamming distance t_m between α and any code word $\mathbf{x}_m$ is defined, and hence their dot product is equal to

$$\alpha \cdot \mathbf{x}_m = n - 2t_m.$$

The decoding criterion can be thought to be either minimizing the Euclidean distance $d_E(\alpha, \mathbf{x}_m)$, or equivalently maximizing the dot product $\alpha \cdot \mathbf{x}_m$, or equivalently minimizing the Hamming distance t_m.

The condition which permits conditional Hamming distance decoding follows from the following theorem.

THEOREM 3.1*a*

There is at most one code word $\mathbf{x}_m$ from a code of length n and minimum distance d such that

$$\alpha \cdot \mathbf{x}_m = n - 2t_m > n - d, \qquad (3.8)$$

when the coordinates of α are ± 1.

Proof:

Let $\mathbf{x}_m{'}$ be a code word which differs from $\mathbf{x}_m$ in d coordinates, so that

$$x_{mi} \neq x_{m'i}, \qquad i \in S; \qquad |S| = d.$$

Then

$$\alpha \cdot \mathbf{x}_m = \sum_{i \notin S} \alpha_i s(x_{mi}) + \sum_{i \in S} \alpha_i s(x_{mi}) = A_1 + A_2;$$

$$\alpha \cdot \mathbf{x}_{m'} = \sum_{i \notin S} \alpha_i s(x_{m'i}) + \sum_{i \in S} \alpha_i s(x_{m'i}) = A_1 - A_2.$$

But

$$A_1 = \sum_{i \notin S} \alpha_i s(x_{mi}) \le n - d;$$

therefore, if $\alpha \cdot \mathbf{x}_m > n - d$, then $A_2 > 0$, so that $\alpha \cdot \mathbf{x}_{m'} < n - d$, as was to be proved.

Condition 3.8 is more commonly met in the form

$$2t_m < d. \tag{3.8a}$$

A first step toward preserving more likelihood information at the output of the detector is to use a quantizer with three-valued characteristic

$$q(L) = \begin{cases} +1, & L \ge T; \\ 0, & -T < L < T; \\ -1, & L \le -T, \end{cases}$$

where T is some threshold which can be set to optimize performance. The output 0 is usually called an *erasure*, and the range from $-T$ to T a *null zone*. Geometrically, this permits α to be any of the grid of points with coordinates ± 1 or 0, as is illustrated in Figure 3.4.

In this case, if s is the total number of erasures and t_m is the Hamming distance between $\mathbf{x}_m$ and α in the unerased coordinates,

$$\alpha \cdot \mathbf{x}_m = n - 2t_m - s.$$

Conditional Hamming distance decoding with erasures follows from the following theorem.

THEOREM 3.1*b*

There is at most one code word $\mathbf{x}_m$ *from a code of length n and minimum distance d such that*

$$\alpha \cdot \mathbf{x}_m = n - 2t_m - s > n - d, \tag{3.9}$$

or equivalently, and more familiarly,

$$2t_m + s < d. \tag{3.9a}$$

The proof is identical to that of Theorem 1*a*.

Whenever Equation 3.8 or 3.9 is satisfied, we say that $\mathbf{x}_m$ is *within the minimum distance* of **α**. Conditional Hamming distance decoding amounts to decoding only when there is some code word within the minimum distance of the received word. We shall call the two types of conditional Hamming distance decoding *errors-only* and *erasures-and-errors* decoding. Three positive features of conditional Hamming distance decoding may be distinguished:

1. Let x_m be the code word actually transmitted; then t, the number of errors, is equal to t_m. It follows that the received word will be decoded correctly if and only if $2t + s < d$. As the occurrences of erasures and errors are statistically independent from bit to bit when the channel is memoryless, the probability of not decoding correctly can be accurately estimated by the Chernov bound techniques of Section 3.1.4.

2. As with any type of conditional decoding, if the decoder happens on a code word within the minimum distance, that word can be announced as its choice, without exhaustive comparison of the distances to all words. A possible decoding method is then to generate a small number of code words which must contain the unique word within the minimum distance, if there is one; this word is readily recognizable. A number of clever schemes[3] use this feature, as does generalized minimum distance decoding which we describe in Section 3.1.3.

3. For the class of BCH codes, it is possible to specify an efficient general algorithm which works whenever condition 3.9 is satisfied, but not otherwise, as we show in Appendix B.

In the next section we introduce generalized minimum distance decoding, which shares these positive features while improving on the performance obtainable with Hamming distance decoding.

3.1.3 Generalized Minimum Distance Decoding. We now suppose that the output of the detector, α, can be any number between -1 and $+1$. Thus the point **α** may lie anywhere within the hypercube on whose vertices lie the code points. In the next section we shall find that the optimum quantizer characteristic, in the sense of minimizing a bound on the probability of not decoding correctly, is

$$q(L) = \begin{cases} +1, & L \geq T; \\ \dfrac{L}{T}, & -T \leq L \leq T; \\ -1, & L \leq -T, \end{cases}$$

where T is some threshold. Thus, except for hard limiting at each end, this quantizer preserves the bit log likelihood ratio in the decoding metric, which we call *generalized distance*.

By limiting $-1 \leq \alpha \leq 1$, we are able to prove the following theorem.

Theorem 3.1c

There is at most one code word $\mathbf{x}_m$ from a code of length n and minimum distance d such that

$$\boldsymbol{\alpha} \cdot \mathbf{x}_m > n - d, \tag{3.10}$$

when the coordinates of $\boldsymbol{\alpha}$ lie between -1 and $+1$.

The proof is identical to that of Theorem 1a; in particular we verify that

$$A_1 = \sum_{i \in S} \alpha_i s(x_{mi}) \leq n - d,$$

since the sum consists of no more than $n - d$ terms of magnitude no greater than 1.

We shall not discuss exhaustive generalized distance decoding, but only decoding when condition 3.10 is satisfied, which we call *generalized minimum distance* or *GMD* decoding.

The points $\boldsymbol{\alpha}$ within the hypercube for which $\boldsymbol{\alpha} \cdot \mathbf{x}_m > n - d$ form a corner of the hypercube centered on $\mathbf{x}_m$, as is illustrated in Figure 3.5

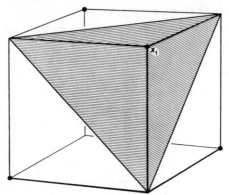

Figure 3.5   Points $\boldsymbol{\alpha}$ for which a GMD decoder will give $\mathbf{x}_1$.

for the (3, 2) code. The points $\boldsymbol{\alpha}$ for which $\boldsymbol{\alpha} \cdot \mathbf{x}_m \leq n - d$ for all $\mathbf{x}_m$, which are the points for which a GMD decoder will fail to decode, form a region in the center of the hypercube including the origin.

It is clear that errors-only and erasures-and-errors decoding are specializations of GMD decoding (since the detector output can be further quantized to ± 1 or 0), and therefore that the performance of GMD must equal or better that of the strictly algebraic decoding schemes. However, it remains to be shown that the GMD information packet can be used in an efficient decoding algorithm. We now show how an erasures-and-errors decoding algorithm can be adapted to do GMD decoding.

For any $\boldsymbol{\alpha}$, let $i_1, i_2, \cdots, i_n$ be such that

$$|\alpha_{i_1}| \le |\alpha_{i_2}| \le \cdots \le |\alpha_{i_n}|; \tag{3.11}$$

since a small magnitude of α corresponds to nearly equal probabilities for the two input signals, we say that by this numbering we have arranged the weights α_i in order of increasing reliability. Let

$$s(\alpha) = \begin{cases} +1, & \alpha \ge 0; \\ -1, & \alpha < 0, \end{cases}$$

and

$$q_k(\alpha_{i_j}) = \begin{cases} 0, & 1 \le j \le k, \quad 0 \le k \le n; \\ s(\alpha_{i_j}), & k+1 \le j \le n. \end{cases}$$

Then the point

$$\mathbf{q}_k = (q_k(\alpha_1), q_k(\alpha_2), \cdots q_k(\alpha_n))$$

is a point with $n - k$ coordinates equal to ± 1 and k coordinates equal to 0, so that if there is a code word within the minimum distance of it, it can be found by an erasures-and-errors decoding algorithm. The point $\mathbf{q}_0$ corresponds to the received word which would have been given by a hard decision detector; $\mathbf{q}_1$ to the same word with the least reliable symbol erased; $\mathbf{q}_2$ to the same word with the two least reliable symbols erased; and so forth up to $\mathbf{q}_n$, in which all symbols are erased. The following theorem shows that if condition 3.10 is satisfied for some $\mathbf{x}_m$, then for at least one of the $\mathbf{q}_k$ an erasures-and-errors decoder working on $\mathbf{q}_k$ will find $\mathbf{x}_m$.

THEOREM 3.2

If $\boldsymbol{\alpha} \cdot \mathbf{x}_m > n - d$, then, for some k, $\mathbf{q}_k \cdot \mathbf{x}_m > n - d$.

Proof:

The idea of the proof is that $\boldsymbol{\alpha}$ lies in the convex hull defined by the $\mathbf{q}_k$. For let

$$\lambda_0 = |\alpha_{i_1}|;$$

$$\lambda_k = |\alpha_{i_{k+1}}| - |\alpha_{i_k}|, \qquad 1 \le k \le n - 1;$$

$$\lambda_n = 1 - |\alpha_{i_n}|;$$

then

$$0 \le \lambda_k \le 1$$

and

$$\sum_{k=0}^{n} \lambda_k = 1,$$

so that the λ_k are like probabilities. Furthermore,

$$\sum_{i=0}^{j-1} \lambda_k = |\alpha_{i_j}|,$$

so that

$$\alpha = \sum_{i=0}^{n} \lambda_k \mathbf{q}_k.$$

Suppose then that $\mathbf{q}_k \cdot \mathbf{x}_m \leq n - d$ for all k. Then

$$\alpha \cdot \mathbf{x}_m = \sum_{k=0}^{n} \lambda_k \mathbf{q}_k \cdot \mathbf{x}_m \leq (n - d) \sum_{k=0}^{n} \lambda_k = n - d,$$

in contradiction to the assumption of the theorem, so that the theorem must be true.

From this theorem we infer that no more than $n + 1$ trials of an erasures-and-errors decoder are needed to produce the $\mathbf{x}_m$ satisfying Equation 3.10, if such exists. A closer examination reveals that even fewer trials are necessary. First, from the proof of the theorem, it is clear that any $\mathbf{q}_k$ for which the corresponding $\lambda_k = 0$ need not be tried; this means that we may begin with all symbols for which $\alpha = 0$ already erased, may erase all symbols with the same magnitude of α simultaneously, and need never erase any symbols for which $|\alpha| = 1$. Second, from the fact that an erasures-and-errors decoder will work only if $2t_m + s < d$, we see there is no point trying the $\mathbf{q}_k$ which have more than $d - 1$ erasures, namely, all the $\mathbf{q}_k$, $k \geq d$; nor is there any point trying the $\mathbf{q}_k$ for which $d - k$ is even, for such a vector will give $\mathbf{x}_m$ only if $t_m \leq [(d - k)/2] - 1$, but then $\mathbf{q}_{k+1}$ must also give $\mathbf{x}_m$. If by a *trial* we then mean an operation in which the $d - 1 - 2i$ least reliable symbols are erased, an erasures-and-errors algorithm used to decode the resulting word, and the decoded code word, if one is found, checked against the generalized distance criterion 3.10, we have the following corollary.

COROLLARY

No more than $(d + 1)/2$ trials are necessary to find the unique code word within the minimum distance of the received word by 3.10, if there is one.

Furthermore, many or all of these trials may succeed, so that the average number of trials may be appreciably less than the maximum.

As an example, let us suppose a word sent from the (3, 1) code whose words are $x_0 = 000$ and $x_1 = 111$, and a received bit log likelihood ratio vector $L = (+2.0, -0.4, -0.2)$. A maximum likelihood decoder would form the dot products $L \cdot x_0 = -1.4$ and $L \cdot x_1 = +1.4$, from which it would choose x_1, which is the optimum choice. An errors-only decoder would require the detector to quantize L to $\alpha_{EO} = (1, -1, -1)$, from which it would choose x_0 as most likely. The action of an erasures-and-errors decoder depends on the erasure threshold T; assuming $T = 1$, the detector would produce $\alpha_{EE} = (1, 0, 0)$, from which the decoder would choose x_1. Assuming the same threshold with a GMD detector, the weight vector $\alpha_{GMD} = (+1, -0.4, -0.2)$ would result. A GMD decoder would then erasures-and-errors decode the two words $(1, 0, 0)$ and $(1, -1, -1)$, obtaining x_0 and x_1 as two possible trial words (trivially, in this case). By the GMD distance measure, the one of these words which satisfies

$$\alpha_{GMD} \cdot x_m > n - d = 0$$

is x_1, for which $\alpha_{GMD} \cdot x_1 = 0.4$; therefore x_1 is the GMD choice.

3.1.4 Bounds on Probability of Not Decoding Correctly. The types of decoding we have been considering—errors-only, erasures-and-errors, and GMD—all have the property that, if x_m is transmitted, the decoder will not decode correctly—that is, either fail to decode or decode incorrectly—if and only if

$$\alpha \cdot x_m \leq n - d, \tag{3.12}$$

from Theorems 1a, b, and c. Equations 3.12 can be rewritten

$$\sum_{i=1}^{n} \alpha(y_i) s(x_{mi}) \leq n - d, \tag{3.12a}$$

where $\alpha(y)$ is the detector characteristic, and $s(x_{mi})$ is as defined in Equation 3.3. Since the channel is memoryless, the sum in Equation 3.12a is of independent random variables.

The Chernov technique[1] gives exponentially tight bounds on the probability that a sum of random variables fails to exceed a given quantity; in this section we use this technique to bound the probability of not decoding correctly. We derive this bound for a general detector realizing some function $\alpha(y)$ of the demodulator output; we then find the detector which optimizes the bound, which is the likelihood detector-quantizer pair described in Section 3.1.

In order to prove optimality, we must assume some kind of symmetry between the inputs, just as to prove that maximum likelihood decoding is optimum, we need to assume all code words equally likely. In most problems this symmetry already exists; however, for the sake of generality, we shall symmetrize the inputs by the following stratagem, which also shows our results to be minimax. We assume a code with words $\mathbf{x}_m$ of n elements from $GF(2)$. Let us now consider the ensemble of 2^n codes, any one of which is obtained by adding a particular n-bit vector to each of the words in the code modulo 2; each of the codes in this ensemble has the same distance properties as the original code. If we choose one of these codes at random, the probability that a particular word $\mathbf{x}_m$ will be represented by any n-bit sequence is 2^{-n}; the probability that any particular bit x_{mi} is 0 or 1 is $\frac{1}{2}$, independent of what any other bit might be.

For each code in the ensemble, and for any detector characteristic $\alpha(y)$, there will be a certain probability that, if $\mathbf{x}_m$ is transmitted, Equation 3.12a will be satisfied. We can define the average probability of not decoding correctly, Pr(ndc), as the average probability of Equation 3.12a being satisfied:

$$\text{Pr(ndc)} = \text{Pr}\left(\mathbf{y}, \mathbf{x}_m: \sum_{i=1}^{n} \alpha(y_i)s(x_{mi}) \le n - d\right). \quad (3.13)$$

If we define

$$f(\mathbf{x}_m, \mathbf{y}) = \begin{cases} 1, & \sum_{i=1}^{n} \alpha(y_i)s(x_{mi}) \le n - d; \\ 0, & \text{otherwise,} \end{cases} \quad (3.14)$$

then Equation 3.13 can be written

$$\text{Pr(ndc)} = \sum_{\mathbf{y}, \mathbf{x}_m} \text{Pr}(\mathbf{y}, \mathbf{x}_m)f(\mathbf{y}, \mathbf{x}_m) = \bar{f}, \quad (3.15)$$

where by the overbar we mean the indicated average, with

$$\text{Pr}(\mathbf{y}, \mathbf{x}_m) = \prod_{i=1}^{n} \text{Pr}(y_i, x_{mi}) = \prod_{i=1}^{n} \tfrac{1}{2} \text{Pr}(y_i \mid x_{mi}). \quad (3.16)$$

$f(\mathbf{x}_m, \mathbf{y})$ can obviously be bounded by

$$f(\mathbf{x}_m, \mathbf{y}) \le \exp\left\{s[n - d - \sum_i \alpha(y_i)s(x_{mi})]\right\}, \quad s \ge 0. \quad (3.17)$$

Substituting Equation 3.17 into 3.15, we obtain

$$\text{Pr(ndc)} \le \overline{\exp\left\{s[n - d - \sum \alpha(y_i)s(x_{mi})]\right\}}$$

$$= \exp[s(n - d)] \overline{\exp\left[-s \sum \alpha(y_i)s(x_{mi})\right]},$$

$$= \exp[s(n - d)] \prod_{i=1}^{n} \overline{\exp\left[-s\alpha(y_i)s(x_{mi})\right]}, \quad s \ge 0, \quad (3.18)$$

where, in order to write the average of a product as the product of the averages, we have used the fact, expressed in Equation 3.16, that over the ensemble of all codes, and with a memoryless channel, the $\alpha(y_i)s(x_{mi})$ are independent random variables. Furthermore, these variables are identically distributed, each with *moment-generating function*

$$g(-s) = \overline{\exp\left[-s\alpha(y_i)s(x_{mi})\right]}$$

$$= \sum_y \sum_x \Pr(y, x) \exp\left[-s\alpha(y)s(x)\right]$$

$$= \sum_y \tfrac{1}{2} \Pr(y \mid 0) \exp\left[s\alpha(y)\right] + \tfrac{1}{2} \Pr(y \mid 1) \exp\left[-s\alpha(y)\right], \quad (3.19)$$

and *semi-invariant moment-generating function*

$$\mu(-s) = \ln g(-s). \tag{3.20}$$

From Equation 3.18, we then have the bound

$$\Pr(\text{ndc}) \le \exp\{n[s(1 - \delta) + \mu(-s)]\}, \quad s \ge 0, \tag{3.21}$$

where we have defined $\delta = d/n$.

Equation 3.21 is valid for any $s \ge 0$ and any detector characteristic $\alpha(y)$. We now consider the problem of minimizing this bound by appropriate choice of s and $\alpha(y)$, or equivalently of finding the maximum exponent

$$E(\delta) = \max_{s,\alpha(y)} -s(1 - \delta) - \mu(-s). \tag{3.22}$$

It is illuminating to maximize first over $\alpha(y)$; in this way we find the optimum detector for any s. Here $E(\delta)$ depends on $\alpha(y)$ only through $\mu(-s)$ and hence $g(-s)$; taking the partial derivative of the latter with respect to $\alpha(y)$, we find

$$\frac{\partial}{\partial \alpha(y)} g(-s) = \tfrac{1}{2}s \Pr(y \mid 0)e^{s\alpha(y)} - \tfrac{1}{2}s \Pr(y \mid 1)e^{-s\alpha(y)},$$

from setting which to zero we determine that $g(-s)$ is minimized when

$$\alpha(y) = \frac{1}{2s} \ln \frac{\Pr(y \mid 1)}{\Pr(y \mid 0)}$$

$$= \frac{L(y)}{2s}. \tag{3.23}$$

Hence the optimum detector consists of a likelihood detector followed by a constant multiplier, which should hardly be surprising. However, for GMD $\alpha(y)$ must lie between -1 and 1; therefore the optimum $\alpha(y)$ is

$$\alpha(y) = \begin{cases} +1, & L(y) \geq 2s; \\ \dfrac{L(y)}{2s}, & -2s \leq L(y) \leq 2s; \\ -1, & L(y) \leq -2s, \end{cases} \qquad (3.24a)$$

which is as we claimed in the previous section. For erasures-and-errors decoding, the $\alpha(y)$ which minimizes $g(-s)$ is

$$\alpha(y) = \begin{cases} +1, & L(y) \geq s; \\ 0, & -s < L(y) < s; \\ -1, & L(y) \leq -s; \end{cases} \qquad (3.24b)$$

and for errors-only decoding, $g(-s)$ is minimized by

$$\alpha(y) = \begin{cases} +1, & L(y) \geq 0; \\ -1, & L(y) < 0, \end{cases} \qquad (3.24c)$$

which is as was claimed in Section 3.12.

Finally, we maximize Equation 3.22 over s by setting the partial derivative

$$\frac{\partial}{\partial s}\left[-s(1-\delta) - \mu(-s)\right] = -(1-\delta) + \mu'(-s)$$

to zero, obtaining

$$1 - \delta = \mu'(-s) = \frac{g'(-s)}{g(-s)}. \qquad (3.25)$$

In this way s, which determines the thresholds of Equations 3.24a and 3.24b, is given as a function of the minimum distance d. It can be shown[1] that $\mu'(-s)$ is monotonically decreasing with s; therefore Equation 3.25 has a solution with $s \geq 0$ whenever

$$\delta \geq 1 - \mu'(0). \qquad (3.26)$$

As s approaches zero, we see from Equations 3.24a, 3.24b, and 3.24c that the three types of decoding become identical; for all three the least minimum distance that may be used is

$$\delta_0 = 1 - \mu'(0)$$

$$= 2p,$$

where p is the probability of bit error

$$p = \Pr(x, y: L(y)s(x) < 0). \qquad (3.27)$$

In other words, none of these three minimum distance schemes is usable unless the minimum distance is at least twice the average number of bit errors, and in these marginal conditions the three schemes are practically equivalent.

3.1.5 Binary Antipodal Signaling with White Gaussian Noise. As an example, we choose one of the few memoryless channels of any practical interest, the white Gaussian channel with binary antipodal signaling. Besides being relatively tractable, such a channel is apparently an adequate model of some space channels.

Briefly, in such a channel the modulator generates every T seconds either a waveform of energy E or its negative. To this waveform the channel adds white Gaussian noise of two-sided spectral density $N_0/2$. The demodulator is a correlator or matched filter, matched to the given waveform. It is well known that under these conditions the output y of the demodulator is a Gaussian random variable which has, under a convenient normalization, mean $\pm E/N_0$ and variance $\frac{1}{2}E/N_0$, where the sign of the mean depends on whether a 0 or 1 was transmitted. We call E/N_0 the *signal-to-noise ratio per transmitted bit*, and denote it by β. The bit log likelihood ratio is then

$$L = \ln \frac{\Pr(y \mid 1)}{\Pr(y \mid 0)}$$

$$= \ln \frac{(\pi\beta)^{-1/2} \exp -(y - \beta)^2/\beta}{(\pi\beta)^{-1/2} \exp -(y + \beta)^2/\beta} = 4y. \qquad (3.28)$$

Thus the matched filter demodulator is itself a likelihood detector, with output proportional to the bit log likelihood ratio; L is a Gaussian random variable with mean $\pm 4\beta$ and variance 8β.

We suppose that on this channel we are going to use a binary code of length n and minimum distance d, and we inquire into the relative performances of errors-only, erasures-and-errors, and GMD decoding, as well as maximum likelihood decoding. Our primary interest is in the case in which the signal-to-noise ratio per transmitted bit β is large.

We know that to do maximum likelihood decoding we represent the series of n bit log likelihood ratios by vectors in n space, and determine the closest hypercube vertex corresponding to a code word. As scaling does not affect the decision regions, we multiply each L by $1/4\beta$ to get a Gaussian variable

$$\mathbf{z} = \frac{\mathbf{L}}{4\beta},$$

whose mean is the hypercube vertex $\mathbf{x}_m$ corresponding to the code word actually sent, and whose variance in any coordinate is $1/2\beta$. Since the coordinates of $\mathbf{z}$ are independent variables, the distribution of $\mathbf{z}$ is spherically symmetric about $\mathbf{x}_m$, and the projection of $\mathbf{z}$ onto any line through $\mathbf{x}_m$ is a one-dimensional Gaussian random variable with mean at $\mathbf{x}_m$ and variance $1/2\beta$. Consider then the line passing through $\mathbf{x}_m$ and some other code word $\mathbf{x}_{m'}$ whose Hamming distance from $\mathbf{x}_m$ is d, and hence whose Euclidean distance is $2\sqrt{d}$. The decision boundary between the decision regions R_m and $R_{m'}$ is the hyperplane which is the perpendicular bisector of this line; a maximum likelihood decoder will certainly decode incorrectly if the projection of $\mathbf{z}$ onto this line is on the wrong side of the midpoint. Thus

$$\Pr(\mathscr{E}) \geq \int_{\sqrt{d}}^{\infty} \left(\frac{\beta}{\pi}\right)^{1/2} e^{-z^2\beta}\, dz$$

$$= \int_{\sqrt{2\beta d}}^{\infty} (2\pi)^{-1/2} e^{-y^2/2}\, dy \qquad (3.29)$$

$$= \Phi(\sqrt{2\beta d})$$

where we have implicitly defined the error function $\Phi(x)$. For large x,

$$\Phi(x) \simeq \frac{1}{x\sqrt{2\pi}} e^{-x^2/2}; \qquad (3.30)$$

therefore, the exponential behavior of the probability of decoding error is given by

$$\Pr(\mathscr{E}) \geq \frac{1}{\sqrt{4\pi\beta d}} e^{-d\beta}$$

$$\simeq e^{-d\beta}. \qquad (3.31)$$

Actually, if there are n_d words at the minimum distance d from any code word,

$$\Pr(\mathscr{E}) \simeq \frac{n_d}{\sqrt{4\pi\beta d}} e^{-d\beta}$$

but the exponent is the significant quantity.

We now use the Chernov bounds of the previous section to get comparable bounds for the three kinds of algebraic decoding. We first note that $\alpha(y) = -\alpha(-y)$, so that

$$g(-s) = \int_{-\infty}^{\infty} dy[\tfrac{1}{2}\Pr(y\mid 0)e^{s\alpha(y)} + \tfrac{1}{2}\Pr(y\mid 1)e^{-s\alpha(y)}]$$

$$= \int_{-\infty}^{\infty} dy\, \Pr(y\mid 0)e^{s\alpha(y)} \qquad (3.32)$$

by symmetry. Thus for errors-only decoding,

$$g(-s) = \int_{-\infty}^{0} dy \, \Pr(y \mid 0) e^{-s} + \int_{0}^{\infty} dy \, \Pr(y \mid 0) e^{s}$$

$$= e^{-s}[1 - \Phi(\sqrt{2\beta})] + e^{s}\Phi(\sqrt{2\beta}), \tag{3.33}$$

where

$$p = \Phi(\sqrt{2\beta}) \tag{3.34}$$

is the bit probability of error. As β becomes large,

$$g(-s) = \begin{cases} e^{-s}, & s \leq \dfrac{\beta}{2}; \\[2ex] \dfrac{1}{\sqrt{4\pi\beta}} e^{s-\beta}, & s > \dfrac{\beta}{2}. \end{cases}$$

$g(-s)$ is minimized by taking $s = \beta/2$; then the exponent $E(\delta)$ is (from Equation 3.22)

$$E(\delta) = -\frac{\beta}{2}(1 - \delta) + \frac{\beta}{2} = \frac{\beta\delta}{2}$$

so that

$$\Pr(\text{ndc}) \leq e^{-nE(\delta)}$$

$$= e^{-0.5d\beta}. \tag{3.35}$$

The exponent for errors-only decoding is therefore one half that for maximum likelihood decoding, so that 3 dB more power is required to achieve the same probability of error when β is large.[2]

For erasures-and-errors decoding, we have

$$\alpha(y) = \begin{cases} +1, & y \geq \dfrac{s}{4}; \\[2ex] 0, & -\dfrac{s}{4} < y < \dfrac{s}{4}; \\[2ex] -1, & y \leq -\dfrac{s}{4}; \end{cases}$$

substituting into Equation 3.32, we get

$$g(-s) = \int_{-\infty}^{-s/4} dy \, \Pr(y \mid 0) e^{-s} + \int_{-s/4}^{s/4} dy \, \Pr(y \mid 0) + \int_{s/4}^{\infty} dy \, \Pr(y \mid 0) e^{s}$$

$$= e^{-s}\left[1 - \Phi\left(\sqrt{2\beta} - \frac{s}{2\sqrt{2\beta}}\right)\right] + \Phi\left(\sqrt{2\beta} - \frac{s}{2\sqrt{2\beta}}\right)$$

$$- \Phi\left(\sqrt{2\beta} + \frac{s}{2\sqrt{2\beta}}\right) + e^{s}\Phi\left(\sqrt{2\beta} + \frac{s}{2\sqrt{2\beta}}\right). \tag{3.36}$$

As β becomes large,

$$g(-s) = \begin{cases} e^{-s}, & s \le 4\beta(3 - 2\sqrt{2}); \\ \left\{ \dfrac{1}{\sqrt{2\pi}[\sqrt{2\beta} - (s/2\sqrt{2\beta})]} + \dfrac{1}{\sqrt{2\pi}[\sqrt{2\beta} + (s/2\sqrt{2\beta})]} \right\} \\ \qquad \exp\left(-\beta + \dfrac{s}{2} - \dfrac{s^2}{16\beta}\right), & s > 4\beta(3 - 2\sqrt{2}), \end{cases}$$

where the breakpoint for s is a root of the quadratic equation

$$-s = -\beta + \frac{s}{2} - \frac{s^2}{16\beta}.$$

Again $E(\delta)$ is maximized by taking s at the breakpoint, where

$$E(\delta) = 4\beta(3 - 2\sqrt{2})\,\delta$$

$$= 0.686\beta\delta,$$

so that

$$\Pr(\text{ndc}) \le e^{-0.686d\beta}. \tag{3.37}$$

Using erasures and errors therefore permits a reduction of power over errors-only decoding of $0.686/0.5$ or about 1.4 dB.

Finally, for GMD decoding, we have

$$\alpha(y) = \begin{cases} +1, & y \ge \dfrac{s}{2}; \\ \dfrac{2y}{s}, & -\dfrac{s}{2} \le y \le \dfrac{s}{2}; \\ -1, & y \le -\dfrac{s}{2}; \end{cases}$$

substituting into Equation 3.32, we get

$$g(-s) = \int_{-\infty}^{-s/2} dy\, \Pr(y\,|\,0)e^{-s} + \int_{-s/2}^{s/2} dy\, \Pr(y\,|\,0)e^{2y} + \int_{s/2}^{\infty} dy\, \Pr(y\,|\,0)e^{s}$$

$$= e^{-s}\left[1 - \Phi\left(\sqrt{2\beta} - \frac{s}{\sqrt{2\beta}}\right)\right] + e^{-\beta}\left[1 - 2\Phi\left(\frac{s}{\sqrt{2\beta}}\right)\right]$$

$$+ e^{s}\Phi\left(\sqrt{2\beta} + \frac{s}{\sqrt{2\beta}}\right). \tag{3.38}$$

As β becomes large,

$$g(-s) = \begin{cases} e^{-s}, & s \le \beta; \\ e^{-\beta}, & s \ge \beta. \end{cases}$$

Taking s again at the breakpoint, we have

$$E(\delta) = \beta\delta$$

and

$$\Pr(\text{ndc}) \leq e^{-d\beta}. \tag{3.39}$$

It follows by comparison with Equation 3.31 that for high signal-to-noise ratios generalized minimum distance decoding has effectively the same probability of error as maximum likelihood decoding.

We saw at the end of the previous section that neither erasures-and-errors nor GMD decoding improved on errors-only decoding in very marginal conditions; in this case all three fail, by Equation 3.34, when β becomes small enough that

$$\Phi(\sqrt{2\beta}) \leq \frac{\delta}{2}.$$

In our experience it is generally true that on very noisy channels GMD decoding is no better than errors-only decoding, while on very clean channels GMD decoding approaches the performance of maximum likelihood decoding.

3.2 Decoding Nonbinary Signals

The concept of generalized distance extends naturally to nonbinary signals just as Hamming distance does. For both, we shall see that the nonbinary problem is reduced to binary by distinguishing only whether two symbols are the same or different and ignoring the value of their difference. The results for the nonbinary case are almost unchanged.

We now let an element x_{mi} of the input sequence $\mathbf{x}_m$ be one of the q symbols x_j, $1 \leq j \leq q$, where normally q would be a prime power so that these symbols could be identified with the elements of $GF(q)$. The information packet put out by the detector will for now be considered to have two components, an *estimate* $\hat{x}$, one of the q symbols, and a *weight* α, $0 \leq \alpha \leq 1$, indicating the reliability of the estimate. The received word $\boldsymbol{\alpha}$ will then be a sequence of n estimates $\hat{x}_i$ with their n corresponding weights α_i.

In the binary case we were able to construct a geometrical picture by letting the sign of α correspond to the estimate of which of the two signals was sent. Here we are denied such a picture, but by defining

$$s(\hat{x}, x) = \begin{cases} +1, & x = \hat{x}; \\ -1, & x \neq \hat{x}, \end{cases} \tag{3.40}$$

we are able to define a dot product

$$\boldsymbol{\alpha} \cdot \mathbf{x}_m = \sum_{i=1}^{n} \alpha_i s(\hat{x}_i, x_{mi}) \tag{3.41}$$

with which we can prove Theorem 3.1 again.

THEOREM 3.1
There is at most one code word $\mathbf{x}_m$ from a code of length n and minimum distance d for which

$$\boldsymbol{\alpha} \cdot \mathbf{x}_m > n - d, \tag{3.42}$$

where $\boldsymbol{\alpha} \cdot \mathbf{x}_m$ is defined in Equation 3.41 and $0 \leq \alpha_i \leq 1$.

Proof:
Let Equation 3.42 be satisfied for some code word $\mathbf{x}_m$ and let $\mathbf{x}_{m'}$ be any word at distance d or more from $\mathbf{x}_m$. Let the sets of places S, T, and U be defined by

$$x_{mi} = x_{m'i}, \qquad i \in S;$$
$$x_{mi} \neq x_{m'i} \quad \text{and} \quad \hat{x}_i = x_{mi}, \quad i \in T; \tag{3.43}$$
$$x_{mi} \neq x_{m'i} \quad \text{and} \quad \hat{x}_i \neq x_{mi}, \quad i \in U.$$

Then

$$\boldsymbol{\alpha} \cdot \mathbf{x}_m = \sum_{i \in S} \alpha_i s(\hat{x}_i, x_{mi}) + \sum_{i \in T} \alpha_i - \sum_{i \in U} \alpha_i = A_S + A_T - A_U;$$

$$\boldsymbol{\alpha} \cdot \mathbf{x}_{m'} = \sum_{i \in S} \alpha_i s(\hat{x}_i, x_{m'i}) + \sum_{i \in T} \alpha_i s(\hat{x}_i, x_{m'i}) + \sum_{i \in U} \alpha_i s(\hat{x}_i, x_{m'i})$$

$$= A_S - A_T + B_U,$$

where we have used Equations 3.43. Now

$$B_U \leq A_U$$

and

$$A_S \leq n - d,$$

since

$$s(\hat{x}_i, x_{m'i}) \leq 1,$$
$$\alpha_i s(\hat{x}_i, x_{mi}) \leq 1,$$

and the number of elements in S is no more than $n - d$. Furthermore, it follows from $\boldsymbol{\alpha} \cdot \mathbf{x}_m > n - d$ that

$$A_T - A_U > 0$$

and hence

$$-A_T + B_U < 0,$$

so that

$$\boldsymbol{\alpha} \cdot \mathbf{x}_{m'} = A_S - A_T + B_U < n - d,$$

as was to be proved.

For errors-only decoding α must be one; for erasures-and-errors decoding it must be one or zero; and for GMD decoding it may be anywhere in the range $0 \le \alpha \le 1$. Defining a symbol error to be the event in which $\alpha = 1$ and $\hat{x} \ne x_{mi}$, and a symbol erasure as the event in which $\alpha = 0$, we find that condition 3.42 is satisfied for erasures-and-errors decoding when the number of errors t and erasures s are such that

$$2t + s < d. \tag{3.42a}$$

We know from Appendix B that nonbinary BCH codes, including the Reed-Solomon codes, can be decoded whenever Equation 3.42a is satisfied, in a number of operations proportional to d^3.

To prove Theorem 2, we again order the received weights in order of increasing reliability

$$\alpha_{i_1} \le \alpha_{i_2} \le \cdots \le \alpha_{i_n},$$

and set up the $n + 1$ erasures-and-errors-decodable vectors $\mathbf{q}_k$ with components

$$q_{ki} = q_k(\alpha_{i_j}) = \begin{cases} 0, & 1 \le j \le k, \qquad 0 \le k \le n; \\ 1, & k + 1 \le j \le n, \end{cases}$$

so that $\boldsymbol{\alpha}$ lies in the convex hull of the $\mathbf{q}_k$. Defining

$$\mathbf{q}_k \cdot \mathbf{x}_m = \sum_{i=1}^{n} q_{ki} s(\hat{x}_i, x_{mi}),$$

we have the following theorem.

THEOREM 3.2

If $\boldsymbol{\alpha} \cdot \mathbf{x}_m > n - d$, *then, for some* k, $\mathbf{q}_k \cdot \mathbf{x}_m > n - d$.

As in the binary case, we can show that no more than $[(d + 1)/2]$ of the $\mathbf{q}_k$ need be considered, so that the number of trials of an erasures-and-errors decoder required for GMD decoding is proportional to d; thus GMD decoding of BCH codes can be done in $\sim d^4$ operations.†

† With Berlekamp's new algorithm, this becomes d^3.

The Chernov bounds on the probability of not decoding correctly can again be derived. Under the symmetrizing assumption that we choose at random one of the ensemble of $(q!)^n$ codes obtained from permuting each of the n elements in the words of a given code in any of the possible $q!$ ways,

$$\Pr(\mathbf{y}, \mathbf{x}_m) = \prod_{i=1}^{n} \Pr(y_i, x_{mi}) = \prod_{i=1}^{n} \Pr(y_i \mid x_{mi})q^{-1},$$

and

$$\boldsymbol{\alpha} \cdot \mathbf{x}_m = \sum_{i=1}^{n} \alpha(y_i)s(\hat{x}(y_i), x_{mi})$$

is a sum of independent, identically distributed random variables, each with moment-generating function

$$g(-s) = \overline{\exp\left[-s\alpha(y)s(\hat{x}(y), x_{mi})\right]}$$

$$= \sum_{y}\sum_{x} \Pr(y, x) \exp\left[-s\alpha(y)s(\hat{x}(y), x)\right]$$

$$= \frac{1}{q}\sum_{y}\{\Pr(y \mid \hat{x}(y)) \exp\left[-s\alpha(y)\right] + \exp\left[s\alpha(y)\right]\sum_{x \neq \hat{x}}\Pr(y \mid x)\},$$

$$(3.44)$$

so that we can bound the probability of not decoding correctly by

$$\Pr(\text{ndc}) = \Pr(\boldsymbol{\alpha} \cdot \mathbf{x}_m \leq n - d)$$

$$\leq \exp\{n[s(1 - \delta) + \mu(-s)]\}$$

where $\delta = d/n$ and $\mu(-s) = \ln g(-s)$. To minimize the bound, we first minimize $g(-s)$ over $\hat{x}(y)$ and $\alpha(y)$. It is clear from Equation 3.44 that $\hat{x}(y)$ must be chosen as that x_j for which the jth *symbol log likelihood ratio*

$$L_j = \ln \frac{\Pr(y \mid x_j)}{\sum_{j' \neq j}\Pr(y \mid x_{j'})} \tag{3.45}$$

is maximum, in order to minimize $g(-s)$. In other words, the best estimate is the transmitted symbol for which it is most likely that the observed output be y. By differentiating Equation 3.44 with respect to $\alpha(y)$ as before, we find that the $\alpha(y)$ which minimizes $g(-s)$ is

$$\alpha(y) = \frac{1}{2s} \ln \frac{\Pr(y \mid \hat{x}(y))}{\sum_{x \neq \hat{x}}\Pr(y \mid x)}$$

$$= \frac{L(\hat{x})}{2s}, \tag{3.46}$$

where

$$L(\hat{x}) = \max_j L_j$$

is the *estimate log likelihood ratio*.

Thus the estimates for all three types of minimum distance decoding are the same. As for the weights, for errors-only decoding α must be one; for erasures-and-errors decoding

$$\alpha(y) = \begin{cases} 1, & L(\hat{x}) \geq s; \\ 0, & L(\hat{x}) < s, \end{cases}$$

and for GMD decoding

$$\alpha(y) = \begin{cases} 1, & L(\hat{x}) \geq 2s; \\ \frac{L(\hat{x})}{2s}, & 0 \leq L(\hat{x}) \leq 2s; \\ 0, & L(\hat{x}) \leq 0. \end{cases}$$

We note that, while in the binary case $L(\hat{x})$ may never be negative, in the nonbinary case there may be a set E of outputs y for which $L_j < 0$, all j—for example, any y for which $\Pr(y \mid x_j)$ is the same for all inputs x_j. Thus in the nonbinary case, even as s approaches 0, whenever $y \in E$, $\alpha(y) = 0$; these outputs always result in erasures. If we define the probability of symbol erasure as

$$p_x = \sum_{y \in E} \sum_x \Pr(y, x),$$

and the probability of symbol error as

$$p_\mathscr{E} = \sum_{y \notin E} \sum_{x \neq \hat{x}(y)} \Pr(y, x),$$

then the exponent for both GMD and erasures-and-errors decoding is positive whenever

$$\delta \geq 2p_\mathscr{E} + p_x.$$

For errors-only decoding we require

$$\delta \geq 2p,$$

where

$$p = \sum_y \sum_{x \neq \hat{x}(y)} \Pr(y, x).$$

3.2.1 List Decoding. A further generalization would be to permit the detector to put out q numbers α_j, one for each of the inputs x_j, indicating the relative probability of each. The received word $\boldsymbol{\alpha}$ would then be a vector of vectors $\{\alpha_{ij}\}$, and the decoding criterion would be to maximize the dot product defined by

$$\boldsymbol{\alpha} \cdot \mathbf{x}_m = \sum_{i=1}^{n} \alpha_{ij}, \qquad (3.47)$$

where j is a function of i and $\mathbf{x}_m$ defined by

$$x_{mi} = x_j.$$

The detector output is called a *list packet,* and decoding with such packets according to the distance measure of Equation 3.47 is called list decoding.

Almost any type of decoding can be fitted into the list decoding framework. For example, for likelihood decoding, we let

$$\alpha_j = \ln \Pr(y \mid x_j);$$

then maximizing Equation 3.47 is equivalent to maximizing $\ln \Pr(\mathbf{y} \mid \mathbf{x}_m)$. The GMD packet $(\alpha, \hat{x})$ is a specialization of the list packet in which

$$\alpha_j = \begin{cases} \alpha, & x_j = \hat{x}; \\ -\alpha, & x_j \neq \hat{x}, \end{cases}$$

as can be verified by comparison with Equation 3.41. An erasure corresponds to the packet γ for which

$$\gamma_j = 0, \qquad all\ j,$$

while an estimate of $x_{j'}$ (without reliability information) corresponds to a packet $\beta_{j'}$ for which

$$\beta_{j'j} = \begin{cases} 1, & j = j'; \\ -1, & j \neq j'. \end{cases}$$

For GMD decoding, Theorem 2 permitted construction of a GMD decoding algorithm with an erasures-and-errors decoder. We show in Appendix C that, in order to prove a theorem like Theorem 2 for list packets, we must constrain packets to be of the form

$$\alpha_j = \sum_{j'=1}^{q} p_{j'}\beta_{j'j} + p_0\gamma_j, \qquad (3.48)$$

where

$$0 \leq p_{j'} \leq 1$$

and

$$\sum_{j'=0}^{q} p_{j'} = 1,$$

so that the list packets lie in the convex hull of the erasure packet γ and the estimate packets $\beta_{j'}$. The GMD packet satisfies Equation 3.48 with $\hat{x} = x_{j'}$, $p_{j'} = \alpha$, $p_0 = 1 - \alpha$, and $p_j = 0$, $j \neq j'$. In Appendix C we show that the optimum list packet satisfying Equation 3.48 is always a GMD packet; therefore the added flexibility of list decoding gains us nothing over GMD decoding, within this framework.

3.3 Discussion

By introducing the generalized distance measure, we have bridged the gap between maximum likelihood decoding, sometimes called probabilistic, and Hamming distance decoding, sometimes called algebraic, though not without compromises. The decoding method is more complex than erasures-and-errors decoding, but not greatly so—in the general-purpose computer decoding structure of Appendix B, erasures-and-errors decoding of a BCH code of minimum distance d takes $\sim d^3$ operations, while GMD decoding takes $\sim d^4$. Also, the decoding criterion is inferior to the optimum likelihood measure, both because it involves hard-limiting of the bit log likelihood ratio, and because it is conditional rather than exhaustive, in the sense of the last paragraphs of Section 3.1. However, we have seen that in at least one case GMD decoding matches the performance of maximum likelihood decoding—another will develop in Chapter 4—and it seems likely that as a general rule GMD is as effective as maximum likelihood decoding on very clean, low-noise channels.

A decoding scheme closely related to GMD is the following. Let the detector be a full likelihood detector, and let the decoder store a complete likelihood packet (i.e., $\Pr(y \mid x_j)$ for all x_j) for each reception y. From the likelihood packet let the decoder also abstract an estimate $\hat{x}$ ($\hat{x}$ is the x_j for which $\Pr(y \mid x_j)$ is greatest) and the estimate log likelihood ratio

$$L(\hat{x}) = \ln \frac{\Pr(y \mid \hat{x})}{\displaystyle\sum_{x_j \neq \hat{x}} \Pr(y \mid x_j)}.$$

These quantities are the same as those used in GMD except that the quantizer has been eliminated; therefore, this scheme, unlike GMD, is invariant to a change in scale. If the minimum distance of the code is d (which, for simplicity of exposition, we assume odd), let the decoder use an erasures-and-errors decoding algorithm to try to decode the following sequence of words: the sequence of estimates; the sequence of estimates with the two least reliable estimates (i.e., those with smallest

$L(\hat{x})$) erased; and so forth, up to the sequence of estimates with the $d - 1$ least reliable erased. Up to $(d + 1)/2$ code words may result; let the decoder then choose that one of these code words $\mathbf{x}_{\hat{m}}$ for which $\Pr(\mathbf{y} \mid \mathbf{x}_m)$ is greatest—i.e., the one closest to the received word in likelihood distance. It should be clear that the set of code words generated will be the same as those generated by a GMD decoder; the difference is that the choice between them is made by the optimal likelihood measure rather than by the generalized distance measure. Therefore the performance of this scheme must be superior to that of GMD, though it is difficult to obtain analytical results showing how superior.

More generally, GMD decoding suggests a class of decoding algorithms in which algebraic techniques would be used to generate a number of code words close in some sense to the received word, and in which these code words would then be compared to the received word by the likelihood distance measure. It seems plausible that, if enough code words were generated, a close approximation to maximum likelihood decoding would become possible, and not just at low noise levels. To find an efficient technique which, given a received word, can generate a set of code words that will with high probability contain that word which is most likely: This is the central problem.

References

1. H. Chernov, "A Measure of Asymptotic Efficiency for Tests of a Hypothesis Based on a Sum of Observations," *Ann. Math. Stat.*, **23**, 493–507 (1952). Our development owes much to efforts at the Massachusetts Institute of Technology to improve the usefulness of this bound in communication theory; see C. E. Shannon, Unpublished Seminar Notes, Dept. of Electrical Engineering, Massachusetts Institute of Technology, Spring, 1956; R. M. Fano, *Transmission of Information*, John Wiley & Sons, Inc., New York, 1961, Chapter 8; and R. G. Gallager, "Lower Bounds on the Tails of Probability Distributions," Massachusetts Institute of Technology Research Laboratory of Electronics, Quarterly Progress Report, No. 77, 277–291, April, 1965, and *Low-Density Parity Check Codes*, M.I.T. Press, Cambridge, Massachusetts, 1963, Appendix B.
2. C. M. Hackett, Jr., "Word Error Rate for Group Codes Detected by Correlation and Other Means," *IEEE Trans. Information Theory*, **IT-9**, 24–33 (1963).
3. E. Prange, "The Use of Information Sets in Decoding Cyclic Codes," *IRE Trans. Information Theory* (Brussels Symposium), **IT-8**, s5–s9 (1962); T. Kasami, "A Decoding Procedure for Multiple-Error-Correcting Cyclic Codes," *IEEE Trans. Information Theory*, **IT-10**, 124–138 (1964); J. MacWilliams, "Permutation Decoding of Systematic Codes," *Bell System Tech. J.*, **43**, 485–506 (1964); L. D. Rudolph and M. E. Mitchell, "Implementation of Decoders for Cyclic Codes," *IEEE Trans. Information Theory*, **IT-10**, 259–260 (1964).

4. Theoretical Performance of Concatenated Codes

This chapter contains the major result of the monograph: a concatenation scheme of reasonable complexity usable at any rate less than capacity. The scheme involves a maximum-likelihood-decoded inner code and a Reed-Solomon outer code, best decoded by generalized minimum distance decoding.

We approach this result by first investigating what the coding theorem has to say about the performance attainable on the superchannel created by the inner code and original channel, under different assumptions about the character of the superchannel. These results can be compared to those obtained with our concatenation scheme to show that the performance of the latter cannot be bettered by any of a large class of others.

4.1 Coding Theorems for Superchannels

The discrete memoryless superchannel seen by the outer coder-decoder pair consists of inner coder, modulator, channel, demodulator, detector, and inner decoder, as we saw in Chapter 1. If the inner code has length N and rate R nats, there are $q = e^{NR}$ inputs to the superchannel. The number of outputs depends on what kind of information packet is delivered by the inner decoder. With an errors-only packet— that is, simply an estimate—there are q outputs; with an erasures-and-errors packet, $q + 1$ outputs; with a GMD packet, q classes of continuous outputs; and so forth.

As for any other memoryless channel, we could in principle calculate the error exponent $E(R_0)$ for the superchannel from its transition probability matrix; then we could claim from the coding theorem that there must exist an outer code of length n and dimensionless rate r such that

$$\Pr(\mathscr{E}) \le e^{-nE(rR)}$$

where the over-all rate $R_0 = rR$. This done, we would have effectively determined the performance obtainable by a concatenation scheme. Even after specifying the type of information packet produced by the inner decoder, however, we remain far from determining the complete transition probability matrix of the superchannel. To calculate the probability of the decoder putting out a certain information packet, given the transmission of a certain code word, would require investigation of the detailed structure of the code used and of the decoding algorithm. Such a calculation, even if feasible, would be unenlightening as well as tedious.

Rather than compute in detail the performance obtainable with a particular concatenation scheme, we prefer to examine representative superchannels whose properties depend only on the coding theorem for the original channel. First we abstract the coding theorem results of Appendix A which are essential to our development. We then prove a convexity theorem which motivates our choice of interesting superchannels. We evaluate the error exponents for these superchannels, and make some comments about their properties.

4.1.1 Detailed Statement of the Coding Theorem. The coding theorem says that there exists a code of length N and rate R such that

$$\Pr(\mathscr{E}) \le e^{-NE_L(R)},$$

and that there is no code of length N and rate R such that

$$\Pr(\mathscr{E}) \le e^{-N[E_U(R) + o(1)]},$$

where $o(1) \to 0$ as $N \to \infty$.

In Appendix A we discuss the computation of $E_L(R)$ and $E_U(R)$ from the channel's transition probability matrix $\{p_{kj}\}$. It turns out that these curves are given by different expressions over different ranges of rate; here we denote the two expressions for $E_L(R)$ by $E_{L0}(R)$ and $E_{Lx}(R)$, and the two for $E_U(R)$ by $E_{U0}(R)$ and $E_{sl}(R)$. In turn, these expressions are given by the maxima of two other functions, $E_0(\rho, \mathbf{p})$ and $E_x(\rho, \mathbf{p})$.

With apologies for the profusion of notation which is necessarily introduced, we now state what these functions and their interrelationships
are.

Let $E_0(\rho, \mathbf{p})$ be defined by

$$E_0(\rho, \mathbf{p}) = -\ln \sum_k \left[\sum_j p_j p_{jk}^{1/(1+\rho)} \right]^{1+\rho}, \tag{4.1}$$

where $\mathbf{p}$ is any probability vector with components p_j:

$$0 \le p_j \le 1;$$

$$\sum_j p_j = 1.$$

Then let $E_{L0}(R)$ and $E_{U0}(R)$ be defined as

$$E_{L0}(R) = \max_{\mathbf{p},\, 0 \le \rho \le 1} [E_0(\rho, \mathbf{p}) - \rho R]; \tag{4.2}$$

$$E_{U0}(R) = \max_{\mathbf{p},\, 0 \le \rho} [E_0(\rho, \mathbf{p}) - \rho R]. \tag{4.3}$$

Clearly, whenever R is such that the ρ which maximizes $E_{U0}(R)$ is
not more than one—in general, for all rates above a critical rate
R_{crit}—these two exponents are equal:

$$E_{L0}(R) = E_{U0}(R), \qquad R_{\text{crit}} \le R \le C. \tag{4.4}$$

Next, let $E_x(\rho, \mathbf{p})$ be defined by

$$E_x(\rho, \mathbf{p}) = -\rho \ln \sum_j \sum_{j'} p_j p_{j'} \left[\sum_k \sqrt{p_{kj} p_{kj'}} \right]^{1/\rho} \tag{4.5}$$

and $E_{Lx}(R)$ by

$$E_{Lx}(R) = \max_{\mathbf{p},\, 1 \le \rho} [E_x(\rho, \mathbf{p}) - \rho R]. \tag{4.6}$$

A change in the order of summations shows that $E_x(1, \mathbf{p}) = E_0(1, \mathbf{p})$;
over a range of rates $R_x \le R \le R_{\text{crit}}$, $E_{L0}(R)$ and $E_{Lx}(R)$ are both
maximized by $\rho = 1$, so that, defining

$$R_{\text{comp}} = \max_{\mathbf{p}} E_0(1, \mathbf{p}), \tag{4.7}$$

both are equal to

$$E_{L0}(R) = E_{Lx}(R) = R_{\text{comp}} - R, \tag{4.8}$$

a straight line of slope -1.

Figure 4.1 illustrates these relationships for typical $E_{L0}(R)$, $E_{Lx}(R)$,
and $E_{U0}(R)$. We have also drawn $E_{sl}(R)$, the tangent to $E_{U0}(R)$ which
passes through $E_{Lx}(0)$, and have labeled the point of tangency R_{sl}.

The upper and lower bounds to the error exponent are related to these curves as follows:

$$E_L(R) = \max [E_{L0}(R), E_{Lx}(R)] \qquad (4.9)$$

$$= \begin{cases} E_{Lx}(R), & 0 \le R \le R_x; \text{ (low-rate segment)}; \\ R_{\text{comp}} - R, & R_x \le R \le R_{\text{crit}} \text{ (straight-line segment)}; \\ E_{L0}(R), & R_{\text{crit}} \le R \le C \text{ (high-rate segment)}; \end{cases}$$

$$E_U(R) = \min [E_{U0}(R), E_{sl}(R)]$$

$$= \begin{cases} E_{Lx}(0), & R = 0 \text{ (zero-rate exponent)}; \\ E_{sl}(R), & 0 \le R \le R_{sl} \text{ (tangent segment)}; \\ E_{U0}(R), & R_{sl} \le R \le R_{\text{crit}} \text{ (high-rate segment exten-} \\ E_{L0}(R), & R_{\text{crit}} \le R \le C \text{ (high rate segment)}, \quad \text{[sion)}; \end{cases}$$

where we have taken care to show that the zero-rate exponent ($R = 0$) and the exponent in the high-rate segment ($R_{\text{crit}} \le R \le C$) are the same for both upper and lower bounds; in these ranges the exponential

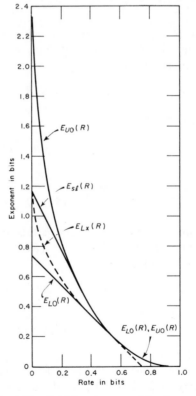

Figure 4.1   Exponents for the binary symmetric channel with $p = 0.01$.

behavior of the probability of error of the best code is precisely known. It has been conjectured[1] that $E_L(R)$ represents the true exponent at all rates; work is continuing to settle this question for $0 < R < R_{\mathrm{crit}}$.

A *binary symmetric channel* has two inputs, two outputs, and a transition probability matrix

$$p_{11} = p_{22} = 1 - p;$$

$$p_{21} = p_{12} = p.$$

By symmetry the optimum probability vector **p** is

$$p_1 = \tfrac{1}{2}, \qquad p_2 = \tfrac{1}{2}.$$

Substituting these values in Equations 4.1 and 4.5, we obtain

$$E_0(\rho) = \rho \ln 2 - (1 + \rho) \ln [p^{1/(1+\rho)} + (1 - p)^{1/(1+\rho)}];$$

$$E_x(\rho) = \rho \ln 2 - \rho \ln [1 + (2\sqrt{p(1 - p)})^{1/\rho}].$$

Figure 4.1 is drawn for the binary symmetric channel with $p = 0.01$.

Similar coding theorems may be proved for many types of channels. The only other appearing in this work is the discrete input, continuous output memoryless channel, where the outputs are a continuous range of real numbers or vectors. The superchannel created when the inner decoder puts out GMD, list, or likelihood packets is one such channel. Another is the white Gaussian channel with binary antipodal signaling and a correlation detector, which we met in the last chapter. A figure of merit for the latter channel is the *signal-to-noise ratio per information bit* E_b/N_0, defined as the ratio of the signal-to-noise ratio per transmitted bit to the rate R in bits:

$$\frac{E_b}{N_0} = \frac{E}{N_0 R}.$$

It is known[1] that the best error exponent for this channel, for fixed E_b/N_0, is achieved when both E and R become very small; generally this involves T, the time to send a single bit, becoming small, and the bandwidth large. For this channel, called the *unlimited bandwidth white Gaussian channel*, it is convenient to introduce the units of *normalized rate*,

$$r^* = \frac{\ln 2}{E_b/N_0},$$

and *normalized length*,

$$n^* = \frac{E_w/N_0}{\ln 2} = \frac{kE_b/N_0}{\ln 2} = \frac{k}{r^*},$$

where k is the number of information symbols in a code word, E_w/N_0 $= kE_b/N_0$ is the signal-to-noise ratio per word, and $\ln 2$ is the conversion factor from bits to nats. Then the coding theorem statement is of the form

$$\Pr(\mathscr{E}) \leq e^{-n*e(r*)},$$

where $e(r*)$ is the normalized error exponent. It can be shown that for the unlimited bandwidth channel the upper and lower bounds to the exponent are identical, and in terms of $r*$ are given by

$$e_L(r*) = e_U(r*) = \begin{cases} (1 - r*^{1/2})^2, & \frac{1}{4} \leq r* \leq 1; \\ (\frac{1}{2} - r*), & 0 \leq r* \leq \frac{1}{4}, \end{cases}$$

which is plotted in Figure 4.2.

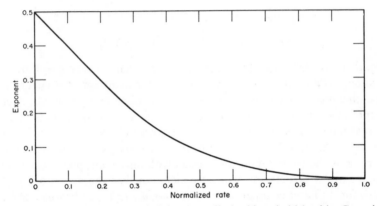

Figure 4.2   The exponent $e(r*)$ for the unlimited bandwidth white Gaussian channel.

Finally, by a minor modification in the proof of the coding theorem, we prove in Appendix A the following result, which has to do with the tradeoff between erasure and undetected error probabilities. There is a criterion β, which is a function of the received word $\mathbf{y}$ and is therefore determinable by the decoder, whose joint distribution function with the event in which the decoder estimate is incorrect satisfies

$$\Pr(\beta(\mathbf{y}) \leq x) \leq K(x)e^{-NE_L(R)};$$

$$\Pr(\beta(\mathbf{y}) \geq x, \text{estimate incorrect}) \leq \frac{1}{K(x)} e^{-NE_L(R)},$$

for some block code of length N and rate R. Here $E_L(R)$ is the same as in the coding theorem; $K(x)$ is a function which equals 1 for $x = \beta_0$ and which increases monotonically and continuously as a function of x, with no upper limit.

Suppose then that the decoder puts out an erasure rather than an estimate whenever $\beta(\mathbf{y})$ is less than some threshold $T \geq \beta_0$. The average probability of erasure will satisfy

$$p_x \leq K(T)e^{-NE_L(R)},$$

and that of error,

$$p_\mathscr{E} \leq \frac{1}{K(T)} e^{-NE_L(R)},$$

where, by proper choice of T, $K(T)$ may be made any number greater than or equal to one. The implication is that by permitting the erasure probability to increase by a factor of K, we can cause the undetected error probability to decrease by at least a factor of K.

4.1.2 Best and Worst Channels. As we have noted, the superchannel is not completely specified. Generally we will know only the average probability of error of the inner decoder, not the detailed transition probabilities from each input code word to each output code word estimate. In this section we prove a lemma which permits us to choose from all channels satisfying a certain incomplete specification the best and the worst—that is, the one with the greatest error exponent, and the one with the least.

We recall from the previous section the function

$$E_0(\rho, \mathbf{p}) = -\ln \sum_k \left[\sum_j p_j p_{kj}^{1/(1+\rho)} \right]^{1+\rho}, \tag{4.10}$$

whose maximum over ρ and $\mathbf{p}$ determines the high-rate segment of the error exponent for a channel with transition probability matrix $\{p_{kj}\}$. For fixed ρ and $\mathbf{p}$, $E_0(\rho, \mathbf{p})$ can be regarded as a function $E_{\rho\mathbf{p}}[p_{kj}]$ of the transition probability matrix $\{p_{kj}\}$. Now the set of all transition probability matrices of the same dimensionality is a convex set, in the sense that if $\{p_{kj}\}$ and $\{q_{kj}\}$ are two such matrices, $\{\lambda p_{kj} + (1 - \lambda)q_{kj}\}$ is also a valid transition probability matrix for any λ in the range $0 \leq \lambda \leq 1$. The following lemma states that $E_{\rho\mathbf{p}}[p_{kj}]$ is a convex function over this convex set.

LEMMA

If $\{p_{kj}\}$ and $\{q_{kj}\}$ are two probability matrices of the same dimensionality, then, for any ρ and $\mathbf{p}$ and $0 \leq \lambda \leq 1$,

$$\lambda E_{\rho\mathbf{p}}[p_{kj}] + (1 - \lambda)E_{\rho\mathbf{p}}[q_{kj}] \geq E_{\rho\mathbf{p}}[\lambda p_{kj} + (1 - \lambda)q_{kj}]. \tag{4.11}$$

Proof:

By substitution of Equation 4.10 into the left side of Equation 4.11 we obtain

$$\lambda E_{\rho\mathbf{p}}[p_{kj}] + (1 - \lambda)E_{\rho\mathbf{p}}[q_{kj}] = -\ln A,$$

$$A = \left[\sum_k \left(\sum_j p_j p_{kj}^{1/(1+\rho)}\right)^{1+\rho}\right]^\lambda \left[\sum_k \left(\sum_j p_j q_{kj}^{1/(1+\rho)}\right)^{1+\rho}\right]^{1-\lambda}; \quad (4.12)$$

by substitution of Equation 4.10 into the right side of Equation 4.11, we obtain

$$E_{\rho\mathbf{p}}[\lambda p_{kj} + (1 - \lambda)q_{kj}] = -\ln B,$$

$$B = \sum_k \left[\sum_j p_j(\lambda p_{kj} + (1 - \lambda)q_{kj})^{1/(1+\rho)}\right]^{1+\rho}. \quad (4.13)$$

But

$$A \le \lambda \sum_k \left[\sum_j p_j p_{kj}^{1/(1+\rho)}\right]^{1+\rho} + (1 - \lambda) \sum_k \left[\sum_j p_j q_{kj}^{1/(1+\rho)}\right]^{1+\rho} \quad (4.14)$$

$$= \sum_k \left[\sum_j p_j(\lambda p_{kj})^{1/(1+\rho)}\right]^{1+\rho} + \left[\sum_j p_j\big((1 - \lambda)q_{kj}\big)^{1/(1+\rho)}\right]^{1+\rho}$$

$$\le B, \quad (4.15)$$

where the inequality in Equation 4.14 is that between the arithmetic and geometric means,[2] and that in Equation 4.15 is Minkowski's inequality,[2] valid since $\rho \ge 0$ so that

$$0 < \frac{1}{1 + \rho} \le 1.$$

But $A \le B$ implies $-\ln A \ge -\ln B$, so the lemma is proved.

By induction from Equation 4.11, one can derive the general convexity relationship

$$\overline{E_{\rho\mathbf{p}}[p_{kj}]} \ge E_{\rho\mathbf{p}}[\overline{p_{kj}}], \quad (4.16)$$

where the overbar indicates an average over any ensemble of transition probability matrices.

Consider, then, the superchannel created by a block code of length N and rate R, a memoryless channel, and a decoder which always puts out an estimate of which code word was sent, and nothing else. This superchannel has then $q = e^{NR}$ inputs and q outputs. Define the probability of error p as the average probability, when one of the code words is chosen at random (with probability q^{-1}), that the decoder estimate fails to match the transmitted code word; then we can say that the superchannel transition probability matrix $\{p_{kj}\}$ satisfies

$$q^{-1} \sum_{j=1}^{q} \sum_{k \ne j} p_{kj} = p;$$

$$q^{-1} \sum_{j=1}^{q} p_{jj} = 1 - p. \tag{4.17}$$

A particular superchannel which satisfies Equation 4.17 is the *equierror superchannel*, which has transition probability matrix

$$\bar{p}_{kj} = \begin{cases} 1 - p, & k = j; \\ p(q - 1)^{-1}, & k \neq j. \end{cases} \tag{4.18}$$

The equierror superchannel is completely symmetric between the inputs and, for any particular input, between all outputs except the one corresponding to that input. As algebraic codes and decoding algorithms share these symmetries, this channel is perfectly suited to algebraic errors-only decoding. The binary symmetric channel is the special case of $q = 2$.

The following theorem shows that the equierror superchannel is the worst of those satisfying Equation 4.17, in the sense that its exponent is least. (In a sense, for a fixed average probability of error, the equierror superchannel is the minimax strategy of nature, while the assumption of an equierror superchannel is the corresponding minimax strategy for the engineer.)

THEOREM 4.1

If $\{p_{kj}\}$ satisfies Equation 4.17, then for any ρ and $\mathbf{p}$

$$E_{\rho\mathbf{p}}[p_{kj}] \geq E_{\rho\mathbf{p}}[\bar{p}_{kj}], \tag{4.19}$$

where $\{\bar{p}_{kj}\}$ is defined by Equation 4.18.

Proof:

Consider the $q!$ channels obtained by relabeling the inputs and outputs of the channel specified by $\{p_{kj}\}$ in every possible way, maintaining the correspondence between them. Clearly all such channels are physically identical and have identical error exponents $E_{\rho\mathbf{p}}[p_{kj}]$, so that their average exponent is also $E_{\rho\mathbf{p}}[p_{kj}]$. Their average transition probability matrix, however, is that of the equierror superchannel. Therefore Equation 4.19 follows from Equation 4.16.

To handle the cases in which the inner decoder adds some reliability information to its estimate, as when it puts out a GMD packet, we need to extend Theorem 1 as follows. Let the weight that the decoder gives an estimate be α; α may take on values over either a discrete or continuous range, but for expository convenience we shall here let it take on the discrete set of values α_k, $1 \leq k \leq K$. Define $p_c(\alpha_k)$ as the average probability that the decoder puts out an estimate which is correct and gives it weight α_k, and $p_e(\alpha_k)$ as the average probability that the decoder puts out an incorrect estimate with weight α_k. If $p_{j'j}(\alpha_k)$ is the probability, given input x_j, that the output estimate is $x_{j'}$ and the output weight is α_k, then

$$q^{-1} \sum_{j=1}^{q} p_{jj}(\alpha_k) = p_c(\alpha_k);$$

$$q^{-1} \sum_{j=1}^{q} \sum_{j' \neq j} p_{j'j}(\alpha_k) = p_e(\alpha_k). \qquad (4.20)$$

It is now straightforward to define an extension of the equierror super-channel, the *GMD equierror channel*, by

$$\bar{p}_{j'j}(\alpha_k) = \begin{cases} p_c(\alpha_k), & j = j'; \\ (q-1)^{-1}p_e(\alpha_k), & j \neq j', \end{cases} \qquad (4.21)$$

and to prove the following extension of Theorem 4.1.

THEOREM 4.1*a*

If $\{p_{j'j}(\alpha_k)\}$ satisfies Equation 4.20, then for any ρ and **p**

$$E_{\rho\mathbf{p}}[p_{j'j}(\alpha_k)] \geq E_{\rho\mathbf{p}}[\bar{p}_{j'j}(\alpha_k)],$$

where $\{\bar{p}_{j'j}(\alpha_k)\}$ is defined by Equation 4.21.

The proof is identical to that of Theorem 4.1.

The GMD channel must be superior to the equierror superchannel, since the latter can be obtained from the former by combining all outputs with the same estimates and different α_k into one; then

$$p = \sum_{k} p_e(\alpha_k);$$

$$1 - p = \sum_{k} p_c(\alpha_k), \qquad (4.22)$$

where the sum is to be regarded as an integral whenever α takes on values over a continuous range. If we know neither $p_e(\alpha_k)$ nor $p_c(\alpha_k)$ precisely, we can upperbound the error exponent of a GMD equierror channel defined by Equation 4.21 by finding the $p_e(\alpha_k)$ and $p_c(\alpha_k)$ which give the maximum exponent, subject to the constraints of Equations 4.21 and 4.22. The result is the *telltale channel* defined by

$$\tilde{p}_{j'j}(\alpha_k) = \begin{cases} 1 - p, & j = j', & \alpha = \alpha_1; \\ 0, & j = j', & \alpha \neq \alpha_1; \\ 0, & j \neq j', & \alpha \neq \alpha_2; \\ (q-1)^{-1}p, & j \neq j', & \alpha = \alpha_2, \end{cases} \qquad (4.23)$$

where α_1 and α_2 are any two distinct weights, whose actual values are clearly irrelevant. In the telltale channel the weight α_1 indicates that the estimate is certainly correct, and the weight α_2 that it is certainly incorrect. The following theorem proves that the telltale channel is the best of this class.

THEOREM 4.2

If $\{\bar{p}_{j'j}(\alpha_k)\}$ is given by Equation 4.21 and $p_e(\alpha_k)$ and $p_c(\alpha_k)$ satisfy Equation 4.22, then for any ρ and $\mathbf{p}$

$$E_{\rho\mathbf{p}}[\bar{p}_{j'j}(\alpha_k)] \leq E_{\rho\mathbf{p}}[\tilde{p}_{j'j}(\alpha_k)],$$

where $\{\tilde{p}_{j'j}(\alpha_k)\}$ is defined by Equation 4.23.

Proof:

Associate with each of the K^2 pairs $(\alpha_{k_1}, \alpha_{k_2})$ the probability

$$\lambda_{k_1, k_2} = \frac{p_e(\alpha_{k_1})p_c(\alpha_{k_2})}{p(1-p)}$$

and the channel defined by

$$p_{j'j}(\alpha)_{k_1, k_2} = \begin{cases} 1 - p, & j = j', \quad \alpha = \alpha_{k_2}; \\ (q-1)^{-1}p, & j \neq j', \quad \alpha = \alpha_{k_1}; \\ 0, & \text{otherwise.} \end{cases}$$

When $\alpha_{k_1} = \alpha_{k_2}$, this channel is the equierror superchannel of Equation 4.18; otherwise it is the telltale channel of Equation 4.23. We verify that

$$\sum_{k_1}\sum_{k_2} \lambda_{k_1, k_2} = 1,$$

from substitution of Equation 4.22, and that

$$\sum_{k_1}\sum_{k_2} \lambda_{k_1, k_2} p_{j'j}(\alpha)_{k_1, k_2} = \bar{p}_{j'j}(\alpha),$$

so that the given channel is the average of a suitably weighted combination of equierror superchannels and telltale channels. All these equierror superchannels are physically identical and therefore have the same exponent, which from the argument preceding Equation 4.22 cannot be superior to that of the GMD channel. The telltale channels are also physically identical and have the same exponent. From Equation 4.16, we know that some weighted average of the exponents of the telltale channel and of the equierror channel is at least as great as the exponent of the GMD channel; but that of the equierror channel is not more than that of the GMD channel; therefore that of the telltale channel is not less than that of the GMD channel.

All these relationships have been proved for $E_{\rho\mathbf{p}}[p_{kj}] = E_0(\rho, \mathbf{p})$, from which $E_{L0}(R)$ and $E_{U0}(R)$ of the previous section are obtained by maximization over ρ and $\mathbf{p}$. We can therefore state that such and such a channel is best or worst only over the range of rates where the upper bound to the exponent is equal to $E_{U0}(R)$ or the lower to $E_{L0}(R)$, since we lack a lemma comparable to Equation 4.11 for $E_x(\rho, \mathbf{p})$. However, it would be surprising if the channels we have described did not retain their extremum properties over all rates, because their symmetry properties give them such intuitive appeal. We do not press this investigation, since as it turns out we already have all we shall need.

4.1.3 Coding Theorems for Concatenated Codes. Let us investigate the performance obtainable with the following simple concatenation scheme. The inner code is a block code of length N and rate R; the inner decoder is a maximum likelihood decoder which puts out an estimate of which code word was sent, with average probability of error p. The outer decoder makes no distinction between inputs, nor, given an estimate, does it distinguish between the outputs other than the estimate. (Any of the algebraic decoders is of this type.) Therefore we regard the superchannel as an equierror superchannel.

In this section we evaluate the coding theorem for superchannels in which the inner code length N is very large. For any N and R we define the *best inner code* as that code for which the average probability of error p is least; then for fixed R we can define the *true error exponent* $E(R)$ as

$$E(R) = \lim_{N \to \infty} \sup - \frac{\ln p}{N}, \qquad (4.24)$$

where for each N the p is that of the best code. The coding theorem shows that

$$E_L(R) \leq E(R) \leq E_U(R);$$

this fixes $E(R)$ over the ranges where $E_L(R) = E_U(R)$ (from Section 4.1.1.):

$$E(0) = \max_{\mathbf{p}, \, \rho \geq 1} E_x(\rho, \mathbf{p});$$

$$E(R) = \max_{\mathbf{p}, \, 0 \leq \rho \leq 1} [E_0(\rho, \mathbf{p}) - \rho R], \qquad R_{\text{crit}} \leq R \leq C.$$

Reversing Equation 4.24, we have

$$p = \exp\{-N[E(R) + o(1)]\},$$

where $o(1) \to 0$ as $N \to \infty$.

We choose the best code as our inner code; then the resulting equi-error superchannel has transition probability matrix

$$p_{kj} = \begin{cases} 1 - \exp\{-N[E(R) + o(1)]\}, & j = j'; \\ [\exp(NR) - 1]^{-1}\exp\{-N[E(R) + o(1)]\}, & j \neq j'. \end{cases}$$

(4.25)

The error exponent of this equierror superchannel is clearly superior to that obtained by using any other block code of length N and rate R as the inner code.

From this transition probability matrix we shall calculate below the upper- and lower-bound error exponents for the superchannel. We can then say that there exists an outer code of length n (in terms of uses of the superchannel) and rate R^* (or e^{nR^*} code words) such that

$$\Pr(\mathscr{E}) \leq \exp[-nE_L(R^*)],$$

and no such code such that

$$\Pr(\mathscr{E}) \leq \exp\{-n[E_U(R^*) + o(1)]\}.$$

In terms of uses of the original channel, the concatenated code has over-all length $N_0 = nN$ and over-all rate $R_0 = R^*/N$. The maximum value of the over-all rate is R; if the dimensionless rate of the outer code is r, $0 \leq r \leq 1$, then $R_0 = rR$. These changes in units are confusing, but easily verified by checking that the total number of words in the code is $e^{nrNR} = e^{nR^*} = e^{N_0 R_0}$.

Calculation of the exponents follows from substitution of Equation 4.25 into the formulas of Section 4.1.1. By symmetry, the probability vector $\mathbf{p}$ for which $E_0(\rho, \mathbf{p})$ and $E_x(\rho, \mathbf{p})$ are maximized is

$$p_j = e^{-NR}, \qquad \text{all } j. \tag{4.26}$$

Substituting Equations 4.25 and 4.26 into Equations 4.1 and 4.5, we obtain

$$E_0(\rho) = -\ln \exp(-\rho NR)[[\exp(NR) - 1]^{\rho/(1+\rho)}$$
$$\times \exp\{-N[E(R) + o(1)]\}^{1/(1+\rho)}$$
$$+ \left(1 - \exp\{-N[E(R) + o(1)]\}\right)^{1/(1+\rho)}]^{1+\rho}; \quad (4.27)$$

$$E_x(\rho) = -\rho \ln \exp(-NR)\{1 + [\exp(NR) - 1]$$
$$\times [2\sqrt{[\exp(NR) - 1]^{-1}\exp\{-N[E(R) + o(1)]\}}}$$
$$\times (1 - \exp\{-N[E(R) + o(1)]\}) + [\exp(NR) - 2]$$
$$\times [\exp(NR) - 1]^{-1}\exp\{-N[E(R) + o(1)]\}]^{1/\rho}\}. \quad (4.28)$$

As N becomes large, the term in square brackets in Equation 4.27 becomes

$$1, \quad E(R) \geq \rho R;$$

$$\exp \{N[\rho R - E(R)]\}^{1/(1+\rho)}, \qquad E(R) \leq \rho R;$$

so that $E_0(\rho)$ becomes

$$E_0(\rho) = \begin{cases} \rho NR, & E(R) \geq \rho R; \\ NE(R), & E(R) \leq \rho R; \end{cases}$$

or, more succinctly,

$$E_0(\rho) = N \min [E(R), \rho R]. \tag{4.29}$$

Similarly, as N becomes large, $E_x(\rho)$ becomes

$$E_x(\rho) = N \min [E(R), \frac{R + E(R)}{2}, \rho R]. \tag{4.30}$$

From Equations 4.29 and 4.30 we derive the three curves

$$E_{U0}(R^*) = \max_{0 \leq \rho} [E_0(\rho) - \rho R^*]$$

$$= NE(R)(1 - r); \tag{4.31}$$

$$E_{L0}(R^*) = \max_{0 \leq \rho \leq 1} [E_0(\rho) - \rho R^*]$$

$$= N(1 - r) \min [E(R), R];$$

and

$$E_{Lx}(R^*) = \max_{\rho \geq 1} [E_x(\rho) - \rho R^*]$$

$$= \begin{cases} N(1 - r)\left[\dfrac{E(R) + R}{2}\right], & R \leq E(R); \\ N[E(R) - rR], & E(R) \leq R, \end{cases}$$

where we have used $R^* = rNR$.

For a given over-all rate R_0, we may vary the inner code rate R and the outer code dimensionless rate r, subject to the constraint $rR = R_0$, in order to maximize performance. We then define

$$E_{CU0}(R_0) = \max_{rR = R_0} NE(R)(1 - r);$$

$$E_{CL0}(R_0) = \max_{rR = R_0} N(1 - r) \min [E(R), R];$$

$$E_{CLx}(R_0) = \max_{rR = R_0} E_{Lx}(R^*).$$

Finally, defining $E_{CL}(R_0)$ by

$$E_{CL}(R_0) = \frac{1}{N} \max \left[E_{CL0}(R_0), E_{CLx}(R_0) \right]$$

$$= \max_{rR = R_0} (1 - r) \left[\frac{E(R) + \min [E(R), R]}{2} \right], \qquad (4.32)$$

we can claim from the coding theorem that if there exists an equierror superchannel with e^{NR} inputs and average probability of error $e^{-NE(R)}$, then there exists a concatenated code of over-all length N_0 and over-all rate R_0 such that

$$\Pr(\mathscr{E}) \le \exp\left[-N_0 E_{CL}(R_0) \right]. \qquad (4.33)$$

We shall discuss the properties of $E_{CL}(R_0)$ and its implications in the next section. Of the plethora of exponents introduced so far, it is the one to remember.

From the negative statement of the coding theorem and $E_{U0}(R_0)$, we can assert that there is no concatenated code of length N_0 and rate R_0 in which the superchannel is an equierror superchannel and

$$\Pr(\mathscr{E}) \le \exp\left\{ -N_0[E_C(R_0) + o(1)] \right\},$$

where

$$E_C(R_0) = \frac{E_{CU0}(R_0)}{N} = \max_{rR = R_0} E(R)(1 - r). \qquad (4.34)$$

Actually, by drawing the tangent from $E_{CL}(0)$ to $E_C(R_0)$ we could assert more, but $E_C(R_0)$ will turn out to be the significant exponent and is the most important exponent to remember.

The foregoing results have to do with the equierror superchannel, presumably the worst of the superchannels derived from the best code, and an inner decoder which puts out estimates only. Suppose now we were to try to improve performance by adding a reliability-indicating weight to the estimate, as in erasures-and-errors or GMD decoding, without relaxing the constraint that the outer decoder treat the inputs symmetrically and make no distinctions between the outputs other than the estimate. From the previous section we know that the best possible resulting superchannel is the telltale channel. We now evaluate the coding theorem bounds for the telltale channel created by the best inner code, whose transition probability matrix is

$$p_{j'j}(\alpha) = \begin{cases} 1 - \exp\{-N[E(R) + o(1)]\}, & j = j', \ \alpha = \alpha_1; \\ [\exp(NR) - 1]^{-1} \exp\{-N[E(R) + o(1)]\}, & \\ & j \ne j', \ \alpha = \alpha_2; \qquad (4.35) \\ 0, & \text{otherwise.} \end{cases}$$

From symmetry we again find the best $\mathbf{p}$ to be Equation 4.26. Then

$$E_0(\rho) = -\ln \exp(-\rho NR)\Big[\big(1 - \exp\{-N[E(R) + o(1)]\}\big) \\ + [\exp(NR) - 1]^\rho \exp\{-N[E(R) + o(1)]\}\Big];$$

$$E_x(\rho) = -\rho \ln \exp(-NR)\big[1 + [\exp(NR) - 1] \\ \times \big([\exp(NR) - 2][\exp(NR) - 1]^{-1} \exp\{-N[E(R) + o(1)]\}\big)^{1/\rho}\big],$$

which both become, as N becomes large,

$$E_0(\rho) = E_x(\rho) = N \min[\rho R, E(R)].$$

Since the lower bound to the exponent is

$\max[E_{L0}(R^*), E_{Lx}(R^*)]$

$$= \max\big[\max_{0 \le \rho \le 1}(E_0(\rho) - \rho R^*), \max_{1 \le \rho}(E_0(\rho) - \rho R^*)\big]$$

$$= \max_{0 \le \rho}[E_0(\rho) - \rho R^*]$$

$$= E_{U0}(R^*),$$

it follows that the upper and lower bounds to the exponent of the telltale channel are identical. In fact, the maximum exponent for fixed $rR = R_0$ is the previously derived $E_C(R_0)$ of Equation 4.34.

We mention without proof that it can be shown that $E_C(R_0)$ is also the upper and lower bound to the exponent for the best superchannel whose output is a list of estimates with corresponding weights, as long as similar symmetry constraints are imposed and the list does not grow exponentially with N.

The essential points to keep in mind are that with concatenation we can achieve at least

$$\Pr(\mathscr{E}) \le \exp[-N_0 E_{CL}(R_0)],$$

but that, without violating the symmetries between the inputs and between the nonestimated outputs, we can achieve no better than

$$\Pr(\mathscr{E}) \le \exp\{-N_0[E_C(R_0) + o(1)]\},$$

no matter how much reliability information we add to our estimates, even with use of maximum likelihood decoding. In the next section we discuss the properties of these two concatenation exponents, $E_{CL}(R_0)$ and $E_C(R_0)$.

4.1.4 Properties of Concatenation Exponents. We saw in the last

section that the error exponent for a concatenated code of over-all rate $R_0 = rR$ is calculable from the two exponents

$$E_C(R_0) = \max_{rR = R_0} (1 - r)E(R) \qquad (4.36)$$

and

$$E_{CL}(R_0) = \max_{rR = R_0} (1 - r)\left[\frac{E(R) + \min\,[E(R),\,R]}{2}\right], \qquad (4.37)$$

when the superchannel is the equierror superchannel derived from the best inner code. When the superchannel is the telltale channel, $E_C(R_0)$ alone gives both the upper and lower bound to the exponent. In this section we discuss the construction of these exponents from the original exponent $E(R)$, and their properties compared to those of $E(R)$.

In general the concatenation exponents can be constructed graphically from the $E(R)$ curve. In Figure 4.3 we use for $E(R)$ the $E_L(R)$ of

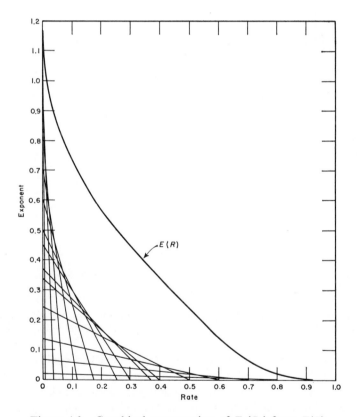

Figure 4.3   Graphical construction of $E_C(R_0)$ from $E(R)$.

the binary symmetric channel with $p = 0.01$, also plotted in Figure 4.1. For fixed inner code rate R, $E_C(R_0)$ is a linear function of R_0 which equals $E(R)$ at $r = R_0 = 0$ and which equals zero at $r = 1$ or $R_0 = R$; $E_{CL}(R_0)$ is another linear function which equals $\frac{1}{2}[E(R) + \min[E(R), R]]$ at $R_0 = 0$ and zero at $R_0 = R$. Clearly the two are equal whenever $E(R) \leq R$. If we then plot these straight lines for all R, the exponent is the convex curve which is their upper envelope. In Figure 4.3 we have illustrated the graphical construction of $E_C(R_0)$. Figure 4.4 plots

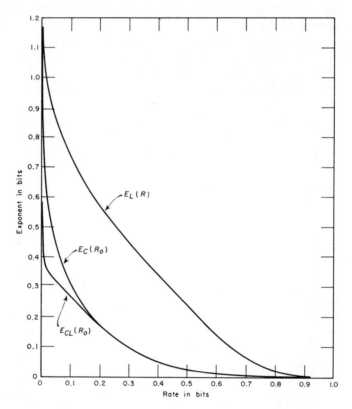

Figure 4.4   Lower-bound error exponent $E_L(R)$ and concatenation exponents $E_C(R_0)$ and $E_{CL}(R_0)$ for the binary symmetric channel with $p = 0.01$.

$E_C(R_0)$ and $E_{CL}(R_0)$ against the original $E(R)$ curve. One could also draw the tangent to the $E_C(R_0)$ curve from $E_{CL}(0)$ to complete the upper bound to the error exponent for the equierror superchannel.

The unlimited bandwidth white Gaussian channel is a rarity for two reasons: Not only is the error exponent $e(r^*)$ known exactly for all normalized rates $r^* = \ln 2[E_b/N_0]^{-1}$, but it can be written explicitly as a function of r^*:

$$e(r^*) = \begin{cases} (1 - r^{*1/2})^2, & \frac{1}{4} \le r^* \le 1; \\ (\frac{1}{2} - r^*), & 0 \le r^* \le \frac{1}{4}. \end{cases}$$

Hence the maximization of Equations 4.36 and 4.37 may be done analytically. Defining the over-all normalized rate $r_0 = rr^*$ and the over-all normalized length $n_0 = nn^*$—as is consistent with our earlier definitions of n^* and r^*—we have

$$e_C(r_0) = \begin{cases} (1 - r_0^{1/3})^3, & \frac{1}{8} \le r_0 \le 1; \\ [(\frac{1}{2})^{1/2} - r_0^{1/2}]^2, & 0 \le r_0 \le \frac{1}{8}; \end{cases}$$

and

$$e_{CL}(r_0) = \begin{cases} (1 - r_0^{1/3})^3, & \frac{1}{8} \le r_0 \le 1; \\ (\frac{1}{4} - r_0), & 0 \le r_0 \le \frac{1}{8}. \end{cases}$$

[It is interesting that these curve segments belong to the self-reproducing (under concatenation) family $(e_0^{1/n} - r_0^{1/n})^n$, of which further stages of concatenation would produce further members.] Figure 4.5 plots these curves and $e(r^*)$.

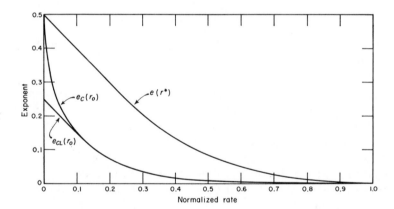

Figure 4.5   True exponent $e(r^*)$ and concatenation exponents $e_C(r_0)$ and $e_{CL}(R_0)$ for the unlimited bandwidth white Gaussian channel.

The most important property of the concatenation exponents is their high-rate behavior. As we have seen, both are identical over the region of high rates, and, as is most easily seen from the graphical construction, *both are nonzero for all $R_0 < C$*, where C is the rate at which $E(R)$ goes to zero. If we choose $E(R) = E_L(R)$, then the coding theorem assures us that there is an inner code with exponent $E(R)$; whatever the actual exponent of the superchannel created by this code, it is not less than that of the equierror superchannel with the same average probability of error; therefore we have proved the following theorem.

THEOREM 4.3
There is a concatenation scheme with over-all length N_0 and rate R_0 such that

$$\Pr(\mathscr{E}) \leq e^{-N_0 E_{CL}(R_0)}$$

where $E_{CL}(R_0) > 0$ for all $R_0 < C$, the capacity of the original channel.

Therefore whatever sacrifice is involved in using concatenation, it is not in the highest rate for which virtually error-free communication can be obtained.

Let us define the efficiencies

$$\eta(R) = \frac{E_C(R)}{E(R)}$$

and

$$\eta_L(R) = \frac{E_{CL}(R)}{E(R)}.$$

The efficiency is a measure of how much longer the over-all length of a concatenated code must be than that of an unconcatenated code to obtain the same probability of error at the same over-all rate; if the efficiency is 0.1, then the concatenated code must be ten times longer. It is here that one is penalized for going to concatenation; however, the penalty need not be too severe. In fact, at zero rate, $\eta(0) = 1$, and $\eta_L(0) = \frac{1}{2}$, as can be seen from setting $r = R = 0$ in Equations 4.36 and 4.37. At high rates, the efficiency goes to zero, as we see from the following argument. Let the first nonzero derivative of $E(R)$ at $R = C$ be the nth; normally n will be 2. Near C, $E(R)$ is approximated by the Taylor series expansion

$$E(R) = \frac{E^{(n)}(C)}{n!}(R - C)^n.$$

For R_0 near C,

$$E_C(R_0) = \max_{rR = R_0} (1 - r)E(R)$$

$$= \max_{R} \left(1 - \frac{R_0}{R}\right) \frac{E^{(n)}(C)}{n!}(R - C)^n.$$

Letting $R_0 = C(1 - \epsilon)$ and $R = C(1 - \delta)$, $0 < \delta < \epsilon \ll 1$, and ignoring all second-order terms in ϵ and δ, we find the optimum δ as

$$\delta = \frac{n}{n + 1}\, \epsilon,$$

whence

$$\eta(R) = \frac{n^n}{(n + 1)^{n+1}}\, \epsilon, \qquad R = C(1 - \epsilon).$$

It follows that while the efficiency approaches zero as $R \to C$, the dropoff in efficiency is not precipitous, being only linear in ϵ. When $E(R)$ has a nonzero second derivative at C, $\eta(R) \simeq 0.15[(C - R)/C]$ for R near C.

Numerical values for the efficiency are given in Tables 4.1 and 4.2 for the two channels we have been using as examples.

TABLE 4.1   Efficiency of Concatenation for the BSC with $p = 0.01$ ($C = 0.92$ Bit)

R (bits)	0	0.1	0.2	0.3	0.4	0.5	0.6	0.7	0.8
$\eta(R)$	1.0	0.41	0.30	0.22	0.15	0.10	0.068	0.043	0.022
$\eta_L(R)$	0.5	0.36	0.30	0.22	0.15	0.10	0.068	0.043	0.022

TABLE 4.2   Efficiency of Concatenation for the Unlimited Bandwidth White Gaussian Channel

r_0	0	0.1	0.2	0.3	0.4	0.5	0.6	0.7	0.8	0.9
$\eta(r_0)$	1.0	0.39	0.24	0.18	0.13	0.10	0.076	0.053	0.033	0.016
$\eta_L(r_0)$	0.6	0.37	0.24	0.18	0.13	0.10	0.076	0.053	0.033	0.016

We see that while the efficiency η is 1 at zero rate, it drops rapidly for low rates, and then declines more slowly for higher rates. However, η_L declines less rapidly at low rates, since it starts at $\frac{1}{2}$ at zero rate.

4.2   Performance of RS Codes as Outer Codes

Theorem 4.3 shows that with concatenation one can achieve exponential decrease of probability of error with block length for all rates below capacity. However, derived as the theorem is from coding theorem arguments, it fails to specify a scheme attaining this performance. In this section we give such a scheme.

Let the inner code be the best block code of length N and rate R, whose average probability of error p satisfies

$$p \leq \exp\{-N[E(R) + o(1)]\}, \tag{4.38}$$

where $E(R)$ is the true error exponent. Let R be such that e^{NR} is a prime power, and let the outer code be a Reed-Solomon code of length $n = e^{NR}$, minimum distance d, and therefore dimensionless rate $r = (n - d + 1)/n$. Then the concatenated code has over-all length $N_0 = nN = Ne^{NR}$ and over-all rate $R_0 = rR$.

Suppose first that the inner decoder passes on to the Reed-Solomon decoder only an estimate, so that the latter performs errors-only decoding. The RS decoder will fail to decode correctly if and only if the actual number of inner decoder errors t is such that

$$2t \geq d.$$

For a formulation similar to that of Chapter 3, let α now be a random variable which equals 1 when no inner decoding error is made and -1 when an error is made; then the RS decoder will fail to decode correctly if and only if

$$\sum_{i=1}^{n} \alpha_i \leq n - d.$$

We can bound the probability that this sum of independent, identically distributed random variables α_i is less than $n - d$ by the Chernov bound techniques of Chapter 3. The random variable α has the moment-generating function

$$g(-s) = \overline{e^{-s\alpha}} = pe^s + (1 - p)e^{-s}.$$

If $\mu(-s) = \ln g(-s)$ and $\delta = d/n$,

$$\Pr(\text{ndc}) = \Pr(\sum \alpha_i \leq n - d) \leq e^{-n[s(\delta - 1) - \mu(-s)]}.$$

To maximize the exponent, we set its derivative with respect to s to zero:

$$\delta - 1 = -\mu'(-s) = -\frac{g'(-s)}{g(-s)} = \frac{pe^s - (1 - p)e^{-s}}{pe^s + (1 - p)e^{-s}},$$

from which we obtain

$$s = \tfrac{1}{2} \ln \frac{(1 - p)\delta}{p(2 - \delta)}$$

and

$$s(\delta - 1) - \mu(-s)$$
$$= -\frac{\delta}{2} \ln p - \left(1 - \frac{\delta}{2}\right) \ln (1 - p) + \frac{\delta}{2} \ln \frac{\delta}{2} + \left(1 - \frac{\delta}{2}\right) \ln \left(1 - \frac{\delta}{2}\right).$$

Now let N become large; then $\delta \to (1 - r)$, $p \to e^{-NE(R)}$, and $(1 - p) \to 1$, so that

$$\Pr(\text{ndc}) \le \exp\left\{-nN\left[\left(\frac{1 - r}{2}\right)E(R) - \frac{\mathcal{H}(\delta/2)}{N}\right]\right\},$$

where $\mathcal{H}(x) = -x \ln x - (1 - x) \ln (1 - x)$. For large N the latter term is negligible; using $nN = N_0$, and picking r and R to maximize the exponent subject to $rR = R_0$, we find

$$\Pr(\text{ndc}) \le e^{-N_0 E_C(R_0)/2}, \qquad (4.39)$$

where

$$E_C(R_0) = \max_{rR = R_0} (1 - r)E(R). \qquad (4.40)$$

In other words, with an errors-only RS decoder we can achieve an exponent of one-half the concatenation exponent $E_C(R_0)$ of the previous section. In particular, we can achieve $E_{CL}(0) = \frac{1}{2}E_C(0)$, which is the true zero-rate exponent for equierror channels.

Second, let the inner decoder have the option of putting out an erasure instead of an estimate, so that the RS decoder does erasures-and-errors decoding. We assume that there is some such scheme in which the average probability of erasure is

$$p_x \le K e^{-NE(R)}, \qquad (4.41a)$$

and of error,

$$p_{\mathscr{E}} \le K^{-1} e^{-NE(R)}, \qquad (4.41b)$$

for any $K \ge 1$. If $E(R) = E_L(R)$ there is such a scheme, as we stated in Section 4.1.1. Letting α now be the random variable which equals -1 when an error occurs, 0 when an erasure occurs, and 1 otherwise, the RS decoder will fail to decode correctly if and only if

$$\sum_{i=1}^{n} \alpha_i \le n - d.$$

The random variable α has moment-generating function

$$g(-s) = p_{\mathscr{E}} e^s + p_x + (1 - p_{\mathscr{E}} - p_x)e^{-s},$$

which, for large N, and for the worst values of $p_{\mathscr{E}}$ and p_x, equals

$$g(-s) = K^{-1} e^s e^{-NE(R)} + K e^{-NE(R)} + e^{-s}.$$

We first choose K to minimize $g(-s)$:

$$K = e^{s/2}; \qquad g(-s) = 2e^{s/2} e^{-NE(R)} + e^{-s}.$$

With this choice of K we then maximize the exponent with

$$s = \tfrac{2}{3}NE(R) + \tfrac{2}{3}\ln\frac{2\delta}{3-\delta}$$

to get, ignoring all terms which are negligible for large N,

$$\Pr(\text{ndc}) \leq e^{-2N_0 E_C(R_0)/3}; \tag{4.42}$$

thus with an erasures-and-errors decoder we can achieve an exponent of $\tfrac{2}{3}E_C(R_0)$, assuming that Equations 4.41a and 4.41b can be satisfied. As one might expect, with this choice of K and s the error probability $p_{\mathscr{E}}$ is the square of the erasure probability p_x.

Finally, let the inner decoder now put out a weight α, $0 \leq \alpha \leq 1$, with its estimate, and let the RS decoder do generalized minimum distance decoding. We let the weight α be some function $\alpha(\beta)$ of the criterion function β introduced at the end of Section 4.1.1, for which

$$\Pr(\beta \leq x) \leq K(x)e^{-NE_L(R)}$$

$$\Pr(\beta \geq x, \text{ incorrect estimate}) \leq \frac{1}{K(x)}e^{-NE_L(R)}; \tag{4.43}$$

$K(\beta_0) = 1$ and $K(x)$ increases monotonically without limit for $x \geq \beta_0$. We shall set $\alpha = 0$ (erase) whenever $\beta \leq \beta_0$; furthermore, if β_1 is such that $K(\beta_1) = e^{NE_L(R)}$, we shall set $\alpha = 1$ whenever $\beta \geq \beta_1$. Define

$$p_c(x)\,dx = \Pr(x \leq \beta \leq x + dx, \text{ correct estimate}),$$

and

$$p_e(x)\,dx = \Pr(x \leq \beta \leq x + dx, \text{ incorrect estimate});$$

then the most unfavorable probability distribution, given Equation 4.43, is

$$\Pr(\beta \leq \beta_0) = e^{-NE_L(R)};$$

$$p_c(x)\,dx = e^{-NE_L(R)}K'(x)\,dx, \qquad \beta_0 \leq x \leq \beta_1;$$

$$p_e(x)\,dx = e^{-NE_L(R)}K^{-2}(x)K'(x)\,dx, \qquad \beta_0 \leq x \leq \beta_1; \tag{4.44}$$

$$\Pr(\beta \geq \beta_1, \text{ correct estimate}) = 1;$$

$$\Pr(\beta \geq \beta_1, \text{ incorrect estimate}) = e^{-2NE_L(R)}.$$

The random variable α' which equals $\alpha(\beta)$ when the estimate is correct and which equals $-\alpha(\beta)$ when the estimate is incorrect has moment-generating function

$$g(-s) = \overline{e^{-s\alpha'}} = \Pr(\beta \leq \beta_0) + e^{-s}\Pr(\beta \geq \beta_1, c)$$

$$+ e^s \Pr(\beta \geq \beta_1, i) + \int_{\beta_0}^{\beta_1} dx[p_c(x)e^{-s\alpha(x)} + p_e(x)e^{s\alpha(x)}]. \tag{4.45}$$

Furthermore, the GMD decoder will fail to decode correctly if and only if

$$\sum_{i=1}^{n} \alpha_i' \leq n - d.$$

Wending our way down a familiar path, we choose $\alpha(x)$ to minimize $g(-s)$ by setting the partial derivative

$$\frac{\partial}{\partial \alpha(x)} g(-s) = -sp_c(x)e^{-s\alpha(x)} + sp_e(x)e^{s\alpha(x)}$$

to zero, obtaining

$$\alpha(x) = \frac{1}{2s} \ln \frac{p_c(x)}{p_e(x)} = \frac{1}{s} \ln K(x), \qquad \beta_0 \leq x \leq \beta_1; \qquad (4.46)$$

we shall check later that $\alpha(x) \leq 1$. Substituting Equations 4.44 and 4.46 into Equation 4.45, we obtain

$$g(-s) = e^{-NE_L(R)} + e^{-s} + e^s e^{-2NE_L(R)} + e^{-NE_L(R)} \int_{\beta_0}^{\beta_1} dx[2K^{-1}(x)K'(x)].$$

$$(4.47)$$

Performing the integral,

$$\int_{\beta_0}^{\beta_1} dx \, [2K^{-1}(x)K'(x)] = 2 \ln \frac{K(\beta_1)}{K(\beta_0)} = 2NE_L(R),$$

which factor we ignore since

$$2NE_L(R)e^{-NE_L(R)} = e^{-N[E_L(R) + \ln 2NE_L(R)|N]} = e^{-N[E_L(R) + o(1)]}.$$

Maximization over s follows from solving

$$(\delta - 1) = -\mu(-s') = -\frac{e^s e^{-2NE_L(R)} - e^{-s}}{e^s e^{-2NE_L(R)} + 2e^{-NE_L(R)} + e^{-s}}$$

to get

$$s = NE_L(R) + \ln \frac{\delta}{2 - \delta}.$$

(Since $\ln K(x) \leq NE_L(R)$, $\beta_0 \leq x \leq \beta_1$, we now verify that in Equation 4.46 $\alpha(x) \leq 1$ when N is large.) Then

$$-s(1 - \delta) - \mu(-s) = N[E_L(R) + o(1)],$$

so that, by proper choice of inner and outer code rate, we can attain

$$\Pr(\text{ndc}) \leq e^{-N_0 E_C(R_0)},$$

where

$$E_C(R_0) = \max_{rR = R_0} (1 - r)E_L(R).$$

This will be the same as the concatenation exponent derived earlier if the true error exponent $E(R) = E_L(R)$. Alternatively, if it is found that for some rates $E(R)$ is greater than $E_L(R)$, then it is only necessary that the relatively weak condition 4.43 be true when $E_L(R)$ is replaced by $E(R)$, in order that this exponent equal that found earlier by coding theorem arguments for the best of the GMD channels, the telltale channel. It therefore seems safe to say that with GMD decoding of RS codes we can do as well as can be done with any outer code and any type of decoding, if the inner decoder puts out a GMD-type packet and no distinction is made between errors.

Our story is nearly told; it remains only to ascertain that the complexity of these schemes is reasonable. All schemes require that the inner decoder be a likelihood decoder, which demands a number of comparisons equal to the number of code words $e^{NR} = n$. In a single over-all block the inner decoder must operate n times, so that the total number of computations required of it is proportional to n^2. If the outer decoder is errors-only or erasures-and-errors, the number of computations required is proportional to d^3, or, since r is fixed, to n^3; if it is GMD, then the number required is proportional to n^4. Furthermore, the complexity of an operation is proportional to $(\log n)^2$ or to N^2. We conclude that, for any fixed R_0 less than C, the total complexity of a concatenated decoder is at worst proportional to N_0^4, and without GMD to N_0^3.†

4.3 Discussion

To recapitulate: we have discovered a concatenation exponent

$$E_C(R_0) = \max_{rR = R_0} (1 - r)E(R),$$

which is greater than zero wherever the original channel exponent $E(R)$ is greater than zero—for all rates less than capacity—and which equals $E(0)$ at rate zero. Not only have we exhibited a specific scheme—

---

† Recently Ziv[4] has exhibited a scheme involving the interlacing of binary codes, for which the probability of error decreases exponentially as the square root of the over-all block length, while the decoding complexity increases only algebraically, at all rates less than capacity. This work was a stimulus to the investigation reported here. Still more recently Pinsker[3] has reported a scheme capable of achieving negligible probability of error for all $R < C$, in which the outer code is a binary convolutional code suitable for sequential decoding, and in which the average number of decoding computations per bit is bounded. These schemes have in common a relatively short inner block code to be decoded by maximum likelihood decoding, which cleans up the channel to the point that an efficient outer code may be used.

GMD decoding of RS codes—which attains this exponent with reasonable decoder complexity, but we have shown that, under certain symmetry restrictions, no scheme using GMD-type information packets, any outer code, and any decoding method can do better. We can attain qualitatively similar performance with errors-only or erasures-and-errors decoding of RS codes, with some savings in complexity, but with a loss of factors of $\frac{1}{2}$ and $\frac{2}{3}$ in the exponent.†

We may therefore use concatenated codes at any rate at which we could use unconcatenated. The only loss is in the magnitude of the exponent; the efficiency $E_C(R)/E(R)$ declines to zero as R approaches C. Consequently, longer codes are required if concatenation is to be used. Unless the necessity of minimizing decoding delay is overriding, however, the length of a code is less important than the complexity of its implementation, where the concatenated code will generally be superior.

Our formulation permits us to think of concatenating more than two codes, but there seems no good reason to do so. More stages would further reduce the exponent without reducing complexity significantly.

It would be interesting to pin down the reason for the discrepancy between $E(R)$ and $E_C(R)$. It might be, of course, that the concatenated structure of the code itself precludes attaining an exponent better than $E_C(R)$, even if full maximum likelihood decoding were done on the over-all code. If this were so, it would completely account for the discrepancy, but it seems unlikely that such a weak structural requirement as concatenation could affect the exponent markedly. Another possibility is that by including information about more inner code words in the information packet passed to the outer decoder, we could do better; however, we have remarked in Section 4.1.3 that, if all inner code words not on the list are treated as equally likely and the size of the list does not grow exponentially with N, no improvement can be obtained. To let the list size grow exponentially with N is not an attractive alternative. We are left with the possibility of introducing some decoding scheme for the outer decoder which does not treat all code words other than the estimate as equally likely. Indeed, if the inner decoder estimate is x_m, it is much more likely that, if x_m is wrong, the correct word is among those within distance d of x_m than that it is among those much farther away. We have been able neither to invent a decoding scheme capable of using such information nor to determine whether such a scheme could offer any improvement.

---

† The similarity between the factors $(\frac{1}{2}, \frac{2}{3}, 1)$ found here and the factors $(\frac{1}{2}, 0.686, 1)$ found in Section 3.1.5 is intriguing, both because the factors are so similar and because they are not identical. The discrepancy may well be due to the relative weakness of conditions 4.41*a* and 4.41*b*.

References

1. R. G. Gallager, "A Simple Derivation of the Coding Theorem and Some Applications," *IEEE Trans. Information Theory*, **IT-11**, 3–17 (1965).
2. G. H. Hardy, J. E. Littlewood, and G. Pólya, *Inequalities*, Cambridge University Press, Cambridge, England, 1952, Chapter 2.
3. M. S. Pinsker, "Some Mathematical Problems of Coding Theory," presented at the 1966 International Symposium on Information Theory, Los Angeles, but unpublished.
4. J. Ziv, "Further Results on the Asymptotic Complexity of an Iterative Coding Scheme, " *IEEE Trans. Information Theory* (Los Angeles Symposium), **IT-12**, 168–171 (1966).

5. Computed Performance of Concatenated Codes

While the theoretical results of the previous chapter are heartening, they have to do with performance in the asymptotic region of very long and complex codes, where only the algebraic or exponential character of complexity and $\Pr(\mathscr{E})$ is important. In this chapter we report the results of a computational program whose purpose is to give a feel for the actual numbers which arise in representative situations.

We suppose ourselves confronted with the problem of achieving a given probability of error at a specified rate on a memoryless channel with known transition probability matrix—a problem more well-defined and -behaved than most real problems. Our response is to construct a list of coding schemes which meet the specifications. Although choice of a specific scheme as the best would normally depend on details of implementation and systems considerations, we find ourselves able to make some general comments on the relative complexity of different schemes. We are pleased to note that the results of Chapter 4 are a useful general guide to code design.

Two types of channels are considered: the equierror channel (in particular the binary symmetric channel) and the binary Gaussian channel. The former is probably the most familiar channel model, while the latter not only typifies situations in which some freedom to choose between modulation and coding is possible, but also, as a model of the channel encountered in deep space telemetry, is of some practical interest.

5.1 Coding for Equierror Channels

The equierror channel models a situation in which the modulator, demodulator, and detector are outside the design province of the engineer, so that he sees a discrete channel with q inputs, q outputs, and an average probability of error p. The simplest example of such a channel is the binary symmetric channel, for which $q = 2$; it has transition probability matrix

$$p_{11} = p_{22} = 1 - p;$$

$$p_{21} = p_{12} = p.$$

Our attention in this section is focused almost entirely on the BSC; however, we look briefly at a more general equierror channel, for which

$$p_{jj} = 1 - p, \qquad \text{all } j;$$

$$p_{kj} = (q - 1)^{-1}p, \qquad j \neq k.$$

For such channels we consider the following types of coding schemes: first, a single, unconcatenated BCH code on $GF(q)$ with errors-only decoding; second, an inner BCH code concatenated with an outer RS code. In the latter case, we either let the inner decoder correct whenever it can (that is, whenever $2T < D$, where T is the number of errors and D is the minimum distance of the inner code), and let the outer decoder do errors-only decoding, counting an inner decoding failure as an error; or we let the inner decoder correct only when the received word is within Hamming distance T_0 of some code word, otherwise erase, and let the outer decoder do erasures-and-errors decoding. With the latter option we frequently find that performance is negligibly affected if, rather than letting the outer decoder correct whenever $2t + s < d$, we require in addition that t be no greater than some threshold t_0. Since the maximum number of RS decoder operations required is approximately proportional to t_0^3, we make the latter restriction wherever possible to reduce complexity. We do not consider generalized minimum distance decoding, because of the difficulty of finding accurate, nonasymptotic probability bounds.

We classify these three types of schemes as S–S (for single stage), E–O (for errors-only), and E & E (for erasures-and-errors). The parameters identifying the codes used are N, K, D, and T_0 for the inner code, and n, k, d, and t_0 for the outer code, where $N(n)$ is the length, $K(k)$ the number of information symbols, $D(d)$ the minimum distance, and $T_0(t_0)$ the maximum number of errors corrected; except for E & E, $T_0(t_0)$ is the greatest integer such that $2T_0 < D(2t_0 < d)$.

Formulas for computing the various probabilities involved are derived and discussed in Appendix D. In general we are successful in finding expressions which are both strict upper bounds and good approximations to the probabilities required. The only exception is the expression bounding the probability of undetected error in the inner decoder needed for E & E schemes, where the lack of good bounds on the distribution of weights in BCH codes causes us to settle for an upper bound which is not a good approximation.

Tables 5.1 through 5.6 are lists of schemes of these types which meet given specifications over certain channels. Tables 5.1 through 5.4 concern a binary symmetric channel with $p = 0.01$; in Tables 5.1 through 5.3 we try to achieve $\Pr(\mathscr{E}) \leq 10^{-12}$ at rates of 0.5, 0.7, and 0.8 bit, and in Table 5.4, $\Pr(\mathscr{E}) \leq 10^{-6}$ at rate 0.7. (For this channel $C = 0.92$ bit and $R_{comp} = 0.74$.) In Table 5.5 we try to achieve $\Pr(\mathscr{E}) \leq 10^{-6}$ at $R = 0.15$ bit for a BSC with $p = 0.1$ (so that $C = 0.53$ and $R_{comp} = 0.32$). In Table 5.6 we investigate the 32-ary equierror channel with $p = 0.01$ (which has $C = 4.86$ bits and $R_{comp} = 4.11$), with specifications of $\Pr(\mathscr{E}) \leq 10^{-12}$ at $R = 4$ bits.

Since the value of a particular scheme depends strongly upon details of implementation and the requirements of a particular system, we cannot say that a particular entry on any of these lists is "best." If minimum over-all block length is the overriding criterion, then a single stage of coding is the best solution. However, we see that using only a single stage to achieve certain specifications may require the correction of a great number of errors, so that almost certainly at some point the number of decoding computations becomes prohibitive. Then the savings in number of computations which concatenation affords may be quite striking.

Notes to Tables 5.1–5.6

$N(n)$ = length of inner (outer) code.

$K(k)$ = number of information digits.

$D(d)$ = minimum distance ($d - 1$ is the number of erasures corrected).

$T_0(t_0)$ = maximum number of errors corrected.

nN = over-all block length.

Comment: E–O = errors-only, E & E = erasures-and-errors decoding in the outer decoder; S–S = single-stage.

TABLE 5.1   Codes of Rate 0.5 Which Achieve $\Pr(\mathscr{E}) \leq 10^{-12}$ on a Binary Symmetric Channel with Crossover Probability $p = 0.01$

(N,K)	D	T_0	(n,k)	d	t_0	nN	Comment
(414,207)	51	25	—			414	S–S
(15,11)	3	1	(76,52)	25	12	1140	E–O
(31,21)	5	2	(69,51)	19	9	2139	E–O
(63,36)	11	5	(48,42)	7	3	3024	"Best" E–O
(63,39)	9	4	(52,42)	11	5	3276	E–O
(63,45)	7	3	(54,38)	17	8	3402	E–O
(127,71)	19	9	(38,34)	5	2	4826	E–O
(127,78)	15	7	(33,27)	7	3	4191	E–O
(127,85)	13	6	(32,24)	9	4	4064	E–O
(127,92)	11	5	(46,32)	15	7	5842	E–O
(127,99)	9	4	(62,40)	23	11	7874	E–O
(31,20)	6	2	(45,35)	11	5	1364	E & E
(31,21)	5	1	(77,57)	21	4	2387	E & E
(63,36)	11	4	(40,35)	6	2	2520	E & E
(63,36)	11	3	(72,63)	10	1	4536	E & E
(63,38)	10	4	(41,34)	8	3	2583	E & E
(63,38)	10	3	(47,39)	9	2	2961	E & E
(63,39)	9	3	(42,34)	9	4	2646	E & E

TABLE 5.2   Codes of Rate 0.7 Which Achieve $\Pr(\mathscr{E}) \leq 10^{-12}$ on a Binary Symmetric Channel with Crossover Probability $p = 0.01$

(N,K)	D	T_0	(n,k)	d	t_0	nN	Comment
(2740,1918)	143	71	—			2740	S–S
(127,99)	9	4	(530,476)	55	27	67310	E–O
(255,207)	13	6	(465,401)	65	32	118575	E–O
(255,199)	15	7	(292,262)	31	15	74460	E–O
(255,191)	17	8	(306,286)	21	10	78030	E–O
(255,187)	19	9	(308,294)	15	7	78540	"Best" E–O
(127,98)	10	4	(324,294)	31	12	41148	E & E
(127,92)	11	4	(1277,1234)	43	5	162179	E & E
(127,91)	12	5	(1084,1059)	25	10	137668	E & E
(255,199)	15	6	(214,192)	23	4	54570	E & E
(255,198)	16	6	(234,211)	24	3	59670	E & E
(255,198)	16	7	(214,193)	22	9	54570	E & E
(255,191)	17	7	(214,200)	15	3	54570	E & E
(255,190)	18	7	(232,218)	15	3	59160	E & E
(255,190)	18	8	(232,218)	15	7	59160	E & E
(255,187)	19	8	(198,189)	10	3	50490	E & E
(255,186)	20	8	(224,215)	10	2	57120	E & E

TABLE 5.3   Codes of Rate 0.8 Which Achieve $\Pr(\mathscr{E}) \le 10^{-12}$ on a Binary Symmetric Channel with Crossover Probability $p = 0.01$

(N,K)	D	T_0	(n,k)	d	t_0	nN	Comment
No single-stage code							
(2047,1695)	67	33	(1949,1883)	67	33	3989603	E–O
(2047,1684)	69	34	(1670,1624)	47	23	3418490	"Best" E–O
(2047,1673)	71	35	(1702,1666)	37	18	3483994	E–O
(2047,1662)	73	36	(2044,2014)	31	15	4184068	E–O
(2047,1695)	67	31	(1477,1427)	51	3	3023419	E & E
(2047,1695)	67	32	(866,856)	31	6	1813642	E & E
(2047,1684)	69	32	(1234,1200)	35	3	2525998	E & E
(2047,1684)	69	33	(763,742)	22	5	1561861	E & E
(2047,1673)	71	34	(804,787)	18	5	1645788	E & E

TABLE 5.4   Codes of Rate 0.7 Which Achieve $\Pr(\mathscr{E}) \le 10^{-6}$ on a Binary Symmetric Channel with Crossover Probability $p = 0.01$

(N,K)	D	T_0	(n,k)	d	t_0	nN	Comment
(784,549)	49	24	—			784	S–S
(127,99)	9	4	(236,212)	25	12	29972	E–O
(127,93)	11	5	(475,459)	17	8	60325	E–O
(255,207)	13	6	(204,176)	29	14	52020	E–O
(255,199)	15	7	(136,122)	15	7	34680	E–O
(255,191)	17	8	(123,115)	9	4	31365	"Best" E–O
(255,187)	19	9	(132,126)	7	3	33660	E–O
(127,98)	10	4	(564,545)	20	2	71628	E & E
(127,92)	11	4	(140,127)	14	5	17780	E & E
(127,91)	12	5	(477,466)	12	4	60579	E & E
(255,206)	14	6	(128,111)	18	8	32640	E & E
(255,199)	15	6	(98,88)	11	2	24990	E & E
(255,198)	16	6	(102,92)	11	1	26010	E & E
(255,198)	16	7	(92,83)	10	4	23460	E & E
(255,191)	17	7	(92,86)	7	1	23460	E & E
(255,190)	18	7	(100,94)	7	1	25500	E & E
(255,190)	18	8	(100,94)	7	3	25500	E & E
(255,187)	19	8	(88,84)	5	1	22440	E & E
(255,186)	20	8	(100,96)	5	1	25500	E & E

TABLE 5.5 Codes of Rate 0.15 Which Achieve $\Pr(\mathcal{E}) \leq 10^{-6}$ on a Binary Symmetric Channel with Crossover Probability $p = 0.1$

(N,K)	D	T_0	(n,k)	d	t_0	nN	Comment
(511,76)	171	85	—			511	S–S
(31,11)	11	5	(59,25)	35	17	1829	E–O
(31,6)	15	7	(54,42)	13	6	1674	E–O
(63,18)	21	10	(51,27)	25	12	3213	E–O
(63,16)	23	11	(35,21)	15	7	2205	E–O
(31,11)	11	4	(40,17)	24	5	1240	E & E
(31,10)	12	4	(43,20)	24	4	1333	E & E
(31,10)	12	5	(47,22)	26	10	1457	E & E
(31,6)	15	5	(116,90)	27	2	3596	E & E
(31,6)	15	6	(45,35)	11	3	1395	E & E

TABLE 5.6 Codes of Rate 4 Which Achieve $\Pr(\mathcal{E}) \leq 10^{-12}$ on a 32-Input Equierror Channel with Probability of Error $p = 0.01$

(N,K)	D	T_0	(n,k)	d	t_0	nN	Comment
(540,432)	57	28	—			540	S–S
(31,27)	5	2	(393,361)	33	16	12183	E–O (both codes RS)
(31,25)	7	3	(3250,3224)	27	13	100750	E–O
(148,125)	13	6	(341,323)	19	9	50468	E–O
(148,121)	15	7	(652,638)	15	7	96496	E–O
(223,196)	15	7	(245,223)	23	11	54635	E–O
(223,192)	17	8	(198,184)	15	7	44154	E–O
(223,188)	19	9	(196,186)	11	5	43708	E–O
(298,267)	17	8	(243,217)	27	13	72414	E–O
(298,263)	19	9	(172,156)	17	8	51256	E–O
(298,259)	21	10	(151,139)	13	6	44998	E–O
(298,255)	23	11	(123,115)	9	4	36654	E–O
(298,251)	25	12	(120,114)	7	3	35760	E–O
(31,26)	6	2	(434,414)	21	7	13454	E & E
(148,125)	13	5	(266,252)	15	2	39368	E & E
(148,123)	14	6	(375,361)	15	6	55500	E & E
(148,121)	15	6	(466,456)	11	2	68968	E & E
(223,196)	15	6	(168,153)	16	2	37464	E & E
(223,192)	17	7	(128,119)	10	2	28544	E & E
(298,263)	19	8	(107,97)	11	2	31886	E & E
(298,259)	21	9	(89,82)	8	2	26522	E & E

TABLE 5.7 $P = 10^{-12}$

R_0	Single-stage (N,K)	T_0	Two-stage (N,K)	T_0	$p_\mathscr{e}$	(n,k)	t_0	r	r_4	nN	η	η_4
0.1	(53,6)	11	(15,5)	3	0.00001	(6,2)	2	0.33	(0.37)	90	0.59	(0.41)
0.3	(178,54)	17	(15,7)	2	0.0004	(23,15)	4	0.65	(0.63)	345	0.52	(0.22)
0.4	(207,83)	18	(31,16)	3	0.0002	(36,28)	4	0.78	(0.74)	1116	0.19	(0.15)
0.5	(414,207)	25	(63,36)	5	0.00004	(48,42)	3	0.88	(0.80)	3024	0.14	(0.10)
0.6	(788,473)	34	(127,85)	6	0.0003	(97,87)	5	0.90	(0.86)	12319	0.064	(0.068)
0.7	(2740,1918)	71	(255,187)	9	0.0003	(308,294)	7	0.95	(0.91)	78540	0.035	(0.043)
0.75	(6552,4914)	130	(511,394)	13	0.0007	(880,856)	12	0.97	(0.93)	449680	0.015	(0.032)
0.8	No code succeeds		(2047,1684)	34	0.002	(1670,1624)	23	0.97	(0.95)	3418490	—	

TABLE 5.8 $P = 10^{-6}$

R_0	Single-stage (N,K)	T_0	Two-stage (N,K)	T_0	$p_\mathscr{e}$	(n,k)	t_0	r	r_4	nN	η	η_4
0.3	(30,10)	5	(7,4)	1	0.0002	(9,5)	2	0.56	(0.63)	63	0.49	(0.22)
0.4	(94,38)	8	(15,7)	2	0.0004	(28,24)	2	0.86	(0.74)	420	0.22	(0.15)
0.5	(112,56)	9	(31,21)	2	0.004	(31,23)	4	0.74	(0.80)	961	0.12	(0.10)
0.6	(230,138)	12	(63,45)	3	0.004	(63,53)	5	0.84	(0.86)	3969	0.058	(0.068)
0.7	(784,549)	24	(255,191)	8	0.001	(123,115)	4	0.93	(0.91)	31365	0.025	(0.043)
0.75	(1672,1254)	39	(511,403)	12	0.002	(286,272)	7	0.95	(0.93)	146146	0.011	(0.032)
0.8	(8060,6448)	126	(2047,1695)	33	0.003	(827,799)	14	0.97	(0.95)	1692869	0.0048	(0.022)

Additional Notes for Tables 5.7 and 5.8

R_0 = over-all rate.

$p_\mathscr{e}$ = probability of decoding error in inner decoder.

r = dimensionless rate of outer code.

r_4 = optimum r as calculated in Chapter 4.

η = length of best single-stage code divided by nN.

η_4 = predicted efficiency of concatenation from Chapter 4.

The tables are of "best" codes, single- and double-stage, which achieve $\Pr(\mathscr{E}) \le P$.

Among the concatenated codes with errors-only decoding in the outer decoder, the "best" code is not too difficult to identify approximately, since the codes which correct the fewest errors over-all tend also to be those with comparatively short block lengths. Tables 5.7 and 5.8 display such "best" codes for a range of rates and $\Pr(\mathscr{E}) = 10^{-12}$ and 10^{-6}, on a BSC with $p = 0.01$; the best single-stage codes are also shown for comparison.

5.1.1 Discussion. From these tables we may draw a number of conclusions, which we now discuss.

From Tables 5.1 through 5.6 we can evaluate the effects of using erasures-and-errors rather than errors-only decoding in the outer decoder. These are

1. Negligible effect on the inner code;
2. Reduction of the length of the outer code and hence the over-all block length by a factor between $\frac{1}{2}$ and 1, occasionally quite close to $\frac{3}{4}$;
3. Appreciable savings in the number of computations required in the outer decoder.

From comparison of Tables 5.2 and 5.4 and of 5.7 and 5.8 we find that the effects of squaring the required probability of error, at moderately high rates, are

1. Negligible effect on the inner code;
2. Increase of the length of the outer code and hence the over-all block length by a factor greater than two.

We conclude that, at the moderately high rates where concatenation is most useful, the complexity of the inner code is affected *only* by the rate required, for a given channel.

These conclusions may be understood in the light of the following considerations. Observe the columns in Tables 5.7 and 5.8 which tabulate the probability of decoding error for the inner decoder, which is the probability of error in the superchannel seen by the outer decoder. This probability remains within a narrow range, approximately 10^{-3}–10^{-4}, largely independent of the rate or over-all probability of error required. It seems that the only function of the inner code is to bring the probability of error to this level, at a rate slightly above the over-all rate required.

Thus the only relevant question for the design of the inner coder is: How long a block length is required to bring the probability of decoding error down to 10^{-3} or so, at a rate somewhat in excess of the desired rate? If the outer decoder can handle erasures, then we substitute the probability of decoding failure for that of decoding error in this question but without much affecting the answer, since getting sufficient minimum distance at the desired rate is the crux of the problem.

Once the inner code has achieved this moderate probability of error, the function of the outer code is to drive the over-all probability of error down to the desired value, at a dimensionless rate near one.

The results of Chapter 4 are a useful guide to understanding these results. Recall that, when the probability of error in the superchannel was small, the over-all probability of error was bounded by an expression of the form

$$\Pr(\mathscr{E}) \leq e^{-nNE_c(R_0)}$$

Once we have made the superchannel probability of error "small" (apparently $\sim 10^{-3}$), we then achieve the desired over-all probability of error by increasing n. To square the $\Pr(\mathscr{E})$, we would expect to have to double n. Actually n increases by more than a factor of two, which is due to our keeping the inner and outer decoders of comparable complexity.

That the length of the outer code decreases by a factor between $\frac{1}{2}$ and 1 when erasures-and-errors decoding is permitted is entirely in accord with the results of Chapter 4, where we found the asymptotic factor of $\frac{3}{4}$ ($\frac{1}{2}/\frac{2}{3}$).

Finally, we observe that, surprisingly, the ratios of the over-all length of a concatenated code of a given rate to that of a single-stage code of the same rate are given qualitatively by the efficiencies computed in Chapter 4—surprisingly, since the bounds of that section were derived by random coding arguments, whereas here we consider BCH codes for the inner code. The dimensionless rate of the outer code also agrees approximately with that specified by Chapter 4 as optimum for a given over-all rate.

In summary, the considerations of Chapter 4 seem to be adequate for qualitative understanding of the performance of concatenated codes on these discrete memoryless channels.

5.2 Coding for Gaussian Channels

In this section we consider the problem of coding for the white Gaussian channel. We ignore bandwidth restrictions, though we find that with concatenation extravagant bandwidths are not required.

We restrict ourselves to binary antipodal modulation of the type described in Section 3.1.5; it is known that no penalty in performance is necessarily invoked thereby. We shall let the amount of energy E per transmitted bit be variable, but shall specify a required signal-to-noise ratio per information bit E_b/N_0, or equivalently a required normalized rate $r^* = \ln 2/(E_b/N_0)$ (see Section 4.1.1).

As inner codes we shall use a family of $(2^{K-1}, K)$ binary BCH codes called *biorthogonal codes*, from the fact that in 2^{K-1}-space the vectors corresponding to the 2^K code words consist of 2^{K-1} orthogonal vectors and their negatives. For the reader who is familiar with maximum-length shift register codes, we might mention that the biorthogonal codes consist of the words in a maximum-length shift register code, with an over-all parity check, and their complements. These codes have the useful property that they provide nearly the maximum separation possible between 2^K code points.[1] The inner decoder will always be a maximum likelihood decoder, or word correlator; in effect we are using the biorthogonal code and binary modulator together as a 2^K-ary modulator.

As outer codes we use BCH codes on $GF(2^K)$, which will be Reed-Solomon codes if K is large enough. Again we permit either errors-only or erasures-and-errors decoding. In the latter case, we have the inner decoder erase if the ratio of the probability of the most likely word to that of the second most likely fails to exceed a certain threshold, which we vary to optimize performance.

Finally, we use an RS code in a third stage of concatenation, using errors-only decoding in the second and third stages.

In Appendix D we discuss bounds on the relevant probabilities. Wherever possible, we use exact probabilities of error for biorthogonal modulation on a Gaussian channel which have been computed elsewhere.[1]

Tables 5.9 through 5.11 are representative of the lists obtained. Table 5.9 gives schemes which have $E_b/N_0 = 5$ ($r^* = 0.14$) and $\Pr(\mathcal{E}) \leq 10^{-12}$; Table 5.10 is for $E_b/N_0 = 2$ ($r^* = 0.35$) and $\Pr(\mathcal{E}) \leq 10^{-12}$; and Table 5.11 is for $E_b/N_0 = 2$, $\Pr(\mathcal{E}) \leq 10^{-3}$. We have included in these tables K_0, the total number of information bits in an over-all block, and N_0/K_0, the ratio of the number of transmitted bits to the number of information bits, which is a measure of the bandwidth required.

Again one cannot pick unambiguously the "best" scheme. However, the two-stage schemes in which K is large enough so that an outer Reed-Solomon code of length less than 2^K can meet the required specifications would seem to be very much the simplest, unless some considerations other than those we have heretofore contemplated were significant.

To organize our information about these codes, we choose to ask the question: For a fixed K and specified $\Pr(\mathcal{E})$, which RS code of length

TABLE 5.9 Modulation and Coding Which Achieve $\Pr(\mathscr{E}) \leq 10^{-12}$ with a Signal-to-Noise Ratio per Information Bit of 5, on a Gaussian Channel

2^K	(n,k)	d	t_0	(n',k')	d'	t'_0	K_0	N_0/K_0	Comment
16384	—			—			14	571.4	S–S
64	(21,15)	7	3	—			90	7.47	E–O
64	(20,12)	9	4	—			72	8.89	E–O
32	(26,18)	9	4	—			90	4.62	E–O
32	(26,16)	11	5	—			80	5.20	E–O
16	(155,136)	11	5	—			544	2.28	E–O
16	(90,67)	13	6	—			268	2.69	E–O
16	(85,58)	15	7	—			232	2.93	E–O
16	(80,50)	17	8	—			200	3.20	E–O
16	(75,43)	19	9	—			172	3.49	E–O
8	(236,184)	21	10	—			552	1.71	E–O
8	(201,138)	25	12	—			414	1.94	E–O
8	(197,124)	29	14	—			372	2.12	E–O
2	(511,358)	37	18	—			358	1.43	E–O
2	(481,310)	41	20	—			310	1.55	E–O
2	(461,254)	51	25	—			254	1.81	E–O
64	(43,37)	7	1	—			222	6.20	E & E
64	(41,33)	9	1	—			198	6.63	E & E
64	(26,22)	5	2	—			132	6.30	E & E
64	(19,13)	7	2	—			78	7.79	E & E
64	(22,14)	9	2	—			84	8.38	E & E
64	(18,12)	7	3	—			72	8.00	E & E
32	(29,23)	7	2	—			115	4.03	E & E
32	(30,22)	9	2	—			110	4.36	E & E
32	(25,19)	7	3	—			95	4.21	E & E
32	(22,14)	9	3	—			70	5.03	E & E
16	(127,108)	11	3	—			432	2.35	E & E
16	(117,94)	13	3	—			376	2.49	E & E
16	(81,62)	11	4	—			248	2.61	E & E
16	(79,56)	13	4	—			224	2.82	E & E
16	(73,50)	13	6	—			200	2.92	E & E
16	(15,11)	5	2	(25,21)	5	2	924	3.25	3–S, E–O
8	(43,36)	5	2	(77,69)	9	4	7452	1.78	3–S, E–O
8	(48,37)	7	3	(48,42)	7	3	4662	1.98	3–S, E–O
8	(63,49)	9	4	(31,27)	5	2	3969	1.97	3–S, E–O
2	(63,45)	7	3	(92,80)	13	6	3600	1.61	3–S, E–O
2	(63,39)	9	4	(92,82)	11	5	3198	1.81	3–S, E–O
2	(63,36)	11	5	(63,55)	8	4	1980	2.00	3–S, E–O

TABLE 5.10   Modulation and Coding Which Achieve $\Pr(\mathscr{E}) \leq 10^{-12}$ with a Signal-to-Noise Ratio per Information Bit of 2, on a Gaussian Channel

2^K	(n,k)	d	t_0	(n',k')	d'	t_0'	Comment
512	(211,167)	45	22	—			E–O
512	(261,209)	43	21	—			E–O
512	(311,271)	41	20	—			E–O
256	(255,195)	61	30	—			E–O
128	(127,97)	31	15	(127,119)	9	4	3–S, E–O
128	(127,99)	29	14	(127,117)	11	5	3–S, E–O

TABLE 5.11   Modulation and Coding Which Achieve $\Pr(\mathscr{E}) \leq 10^{-3}$ with a Signal-to-Noise Ratio per Information Bit of 2, on a Gaussian Channel

2^K	(n,k)	d	t_0	Comment
16384	—			S–S
256	(37,27)	11	5	E–O
256	(45,37)	9	4	E–O
128	(48,34)	15	7	E–O
128	(50,38)	13	6	E–O
64	(895,719)	91	45	E–O

$2^K - 1$ requires the minimum signal-to-noise ratio per information bit? Tables 5.12 through 5.14 answer this question for $K \leq 9$ (after which the computer overflowed) and for $\Pr(\mathscr{E}) = 10^{-3}, 10^{-6}$, and 10^{-12}. Except in Table 5.14, we have considered only errors-only decoding, since Table 5.14 shows that, even for $\Pr(\mathscr{E}) = 10^{-12}$, allowing erasures-and-errors decoding improves E_b/N_0 very little, to the accuracy of our bounds, and does not affect the character of the results. The E_b/N_0 needed to achieve the required probability of error without coding, for $K \leq 20$, is also indicated. In Table 5.14 we record $p_{\mathscr{E}}$, the probability of decoding error in the inner decoder.

5.2.1 Discussion. Let us first turn our attention to Table 5.9, which has the richest selection of diverse schemes, while being entirely representative of all the lists we generated. Certain similarities to the lists for discrete memoryless channels are immediately evident. For instance, the use of erasures allows some shortening and simplification of the outer decoder, though not as much as before. Also, for fixed K, going to two stages of algebraic coding rather than one lessens the computational demands on the decoders at the price of much increased block length.

However, it seems clear that it is more efficient to let K become large enough so that two stages of algebraic coding are unnecessary, and in fact large enough that a single RS code can be used as the outer code.

TABLE 5.12   Minimum E_b/N_0 Achievable on a Gaussian Channel without and with an RS Outer Code, for $Pr(\mathscr{E}) = 10^{-3}$

K	S–S	E–O	t_0
1	4.78		
2	5.42		
3	4.26	4.23	1
4	3.57	3.11	3
5	3.12	2.41	5
6	2.81	2.02	9
7	2.59	1.77	18
8	2.41	1.61	33
9	2.28	1.50	62
10	2.16		
15	1.85		
20	1.65		

TABLE 5.13   Minimum E_b/N_0 Achievable on a Gaussian Channel without and with an RS Outer Code, for $Pr(\mathscr{E}) = 10^{-6}$

K	S–S	E–O	t_0
1	11.30		
2	11.96		
3	8.68	7.34	1
4	6.92	4.59	3
5	5.83	3.19	5
6	5.09	2.44	10
7	4.56	2.01	19
8	4.16	1.76	34
9	3.85	1.60	64
10	3.60		
15	2.85		
20	2.45		

TABLE 5.14 $\Pr(\mathscr{E}) = 10^{-12}$

K	S–S	E–O	t_0	$p_\mathscr{E}$	E & E
1	24.74				
2	25.42				
3	17.67	13.53	1	0.0000002	13.60
4	13.67	7.45	3	0.0001	6.86
5	11.23	4.54	6	0.002	4.25
6	9.60	3.13	11	0.009	3.02
7	8.43	2.40	20	0.02	2.38
8	7.55	1.98	36	0.036	
9	6.86	1.73	67	0.05	
10	6.31				
15	4.70				
20	3.84				

As K falls below this size, the complexity of the outer codes needed would seem to increase much more rapidly than that of the inner decreases, while for larger K the reverse is true. The explanation is that a certain K is required to drive the probability of decoding error in the inner decoder down to the point where algebraic coding techniques become powerful, at somewhat less than the final signal-to-noise ratio per information bit. However, once this moderate probability has been achieved, it would seem to be wasteful to use modulation techniques to drive it much lower by increasing K. Tables 5.10 and 5.11 illustrate this point by showing that this critical K is not much affected by an enormous change in required $\Pr(\mathscr{E})$; Table 5.14 shows that the inner decoder probability of error is greater than 10^{-3} for all but the simplest codes.

Since the RS codes are the most efficient of the BCH class with respect to the number of check digits required to achieve a certain minimum distance and hence error-correction capability, another important effect of increasing K is to make the symbol field $GF(2^K)$ large enough that RS codes of the necessary block lengths can be realized. Once K is large enough to do this, further increases result in no further increase of efficiency in this respect.

One may remark that in Tables 5.12 through 5.14 all the RS codes have approximately the same dimensionless rate. The cause seems to be that E_b/N_0 varies over a relatively narrow range, so that the optimum r, which is a function of E_b/N_0, varies little. For example, at $E_b/N_0 = 2.1$, the over-all normalized rate $r_0 = \frac{1}{3}$, and for this r_0 the development of Chapter 4 shows that r should be $r_0^{1/3} = 0.69$. Actually, the (63, 45) 9-error-correcting RS code which attains $E_b/N_0 = 2.02$ at $\Pr(\mathscr{E}) = 10^{-3}$

has $r = 0.71$. For smaller E_b/N_0, r increases slightly, and for larger, it decreases.

We would expect from Chapter 4 that to square the probability of error, we should double the over-all normalized length of the code; in this case this is done by increasing K by 1, which doubles n.

Finally, from Chapter 4 we would expect that, for the same code and E_b/N_0, if we can achieve $\Pr(\mathscr{E}) = 10^{-9}$ with errors-only decoding, we can achieve $\Pr(\mathscr{E}) = 10^{-12}$ with erasures-and-errors decoding. But for all but small K, we can achieve $\Pr(\mathscr{E}) = 10^{-9}$ with errors-only decoding for E_b/N_0 only slightly smaller than that for which we can achieve $\Pr(\mathscr{E}) = 10^{-12}$. Therefore we do not expect erasures to help much; actually the improvement they yield is even less than this argument would suggest, which probably indicates that we are not yet in the asymptotic region.

5.3 Summary

We have seen that the results of Chapter 4 are a useful guide to understanding concatenated codes of practical, nonasymptotic lengths. However, these computations yield insight of another kind. A clear division between the functions of the inner and outer codes emerges: The inner code and decoder must be chosen to achieve a moderate probability of error—say 10^{-3}—at slightly greater than the required rate; then the outer RS code drives the over-all probability of error as low as desired, at a dimensionless rate near one.

To date, work in coding theory has focused largely on the problem of achieving negligibly small probabilities of error. We now see that the existence of Reed-Solomon codes solves this problem whenever the problem of achieving a quite moderate probability of error can be solved. For high-performance applications, effort should therefore be concentrated on finding schemes of high rate which are able merely to keep from complete breakdown; even from an error rate of 1 in 50 we can salvage an over-all probability of error of 10^{-12} with a (127,87) RS code, as we see from Table 5.14. It is also in the inner decoder that the effects of short-term channel memory can best be handled. One suspects that the algebraic approach will be rather ineffective in these areas; what will be required will be schemes directly motivated by and closely matched to the channel's actual, physical behavior.

Reference

1. S. W. Golomb *et al.*, *Digital Communications with Space Applications*, Prentice-Hall, Englewood Cliffs, New Jersey, 1964. See particularly Chapter 7.

Appendix A.   The Coding Theorem for Discrete Memoryless Channels

In its most modern form, the coding theorem consists of exponential bounds on the probability of error achievable by the best code of length N and rate R. In this Appendix we reproduce the development of the lower-bound error exponent $E_L(R)$ which is due to Gallager,[3] with a slight extension which crudely bounds the tradeoff between erasure and error probability; much of this extension is also due to Gallager.[4] We also give without proof expressions for the upper bound exponent $E_U(R)$, due to Shannon, Gallager, and Berlekamp.[5]

We assume a discrete memoryless channel with transition probability matrix

$$p_{kj} = \Pr(y_k \mid x_j), \qquad 1 \le j \le J, \qquad 1 \le k \le K. \qquad (A.1)$$

A code of length N and rate R consists of $M = e^{NR}$ input sequences of length N:

$$\mathbf{x}_m = \{x_{mi}\} = (x_{m1}, \cdots, x_{mN}), \qquad 1 \le m \le M = e^{NR}.$$

A received word $\mathbf{y} = \{y_i\}$ consists of a sequence of N channel outputs. The receiver is assumed to perform a modified kind of maximum likelihood decoding, which we call maximum likelihood decoding with decoding erasures; it consists of computing from $\mathbf{y}$

$$\Pr(\mathbf{y} \mid \mathbf{x}_m) = \prod_{i=1}^{N} \Pr(y_i \mid x_{mi}) \qquad (A.2)$$

106

for all code words $\mathbf{x}_m$, and choosing $\mathbf{x}_{\hat{m}}$ iff

$$\Pr(\mathbf{y} \mid \mathbf{x}_{\hat{m}}) > e^{\beta} \Pr(\mathbf{y} \mid \mathbf{x}_m) \quad \text{for all} \quad m \neq \hat{m}, \tag{A.3}$$

where β is any nonnegative number. If no code word satisfies Equation A.3, then the decoder signals an erasure. If $\beta = 0$, this scheme reduces to ordinary maximum likelihood decoding.

If $\mathbf{x}_m$ is sent, an erasure occurs if $\mathbf{y}$ is such that Equation A.3 is satisfied for no $\hat{m}$, and a decoding error if $\mathbf{y}$ is such that Equation A.3 is satisfied for some $\hat{m} \neq m$. Defining p_{mx} and $p_{m\mathcal{E}}$ as the probabilities of the former and latter events, we have

$$p_{mx} = \sum_{\mathbf{y}} \Pr(\mathbf{y} \mid \mathbf{x}_m)\phi_{mx}(\mathbf{y}); \tag{A.4}$$

$$p_{m\mathcal{E}} = \sum_{\mathbf{y}} \Pr(\mathbf{y} \mid \mathbf{x}_m)\phi_{m\mathcal{E}}(\mathbf{y}), \tag{A.5}$$

where

$$\phi_{mx}(\mathbf{y}) = \begin{cases} 1, & \text{if Equation A.3 unsatisfied, all } \hat{m}; \\ 0, & \text{otherwise}; \end{cases} \tag{A.6}$$

$$\phi_{m\mathcal{E}}(\mathbf{y}) = \begin{cases} 1, & \text{if Equation A.3 satisfied, some } \hat{m} \neq m; \\ 0, & \text{otherwise}. \end{cases} \tag{A.7}$$

We can upperbound the functions in Equations A.6 and A.7 by the functions

$$\phi'_{mx}(\mathbf{y}) = \begin{cases} 1, & \text{if } \Pr(\mathbf{y} \mid \mathbf{x}_m) \leq e^{\beta} \Pr(\mathbf{y} \mid \mathbf{x}_{\hat{m}}), \text{ some } \hat{m} \neq m; \\ 0, & \text{otherwise}; \end{cases} \tag{A.8}$$

$$\phi'_{m\mathcal{E}}(\mathbf{y}) = \begin{cases} 1, & \text{if } \Pr(\mathbf{y} \mid \mathbf{x}_{\hat{m}}) \geq e^{\beta} \Pr(\mathbf{y} \mid \mathbf{x}_m), \text{ some } \hat{m} \neq m; \\ 0, & \text{otherwise}, \end{cases} \tag{A.9}$$

since whenever ϕ_{mx} is 1, ϕ'_{mx} must be 1, and similarly with $\phi_{m\mathcal{E}}$. ϕ'_{mx} is upperbounded by

$$\phi'_{mx}(\mathbf{y}) \leq \left[\frac{\sum_{\hat{m} \neq m} [\Pr(\mathbf{y} \mid \mathbf{x}_{\hat{m}})e^{\beta}]^{1/1+\rho}}{\Pr(\mathbf{y} \mid \mathbf{x}_m)^{1/1+\rho}} \right]^{\rho}, \quad \rho \geq 0, \tag{A.10}$$

as is verified by separate examination of the conditions under which ϕ'_{mx} is 1 and 0 in Equation A.8; similarly

$$\phi'_{m\mathcal{E}}(\mathbf{y}) \leq \left[\frac{\sum_{\hat{m} \neq m} \Pr(\mathbf{y} \mid \mathbf{x}_{\hat{m}})^{1/1+\rho}}{[e^{\beta} \Pr(\mathbf{y} \mid \mathbf{x}_m)]^{1/1+\rho}} \right]^{\rho}, \quad \rho \geq 0. \tag{A.11}$$

Substituting Equations A.10 and A.11 in Equations A.4 and A.5, we have

$$P_{mx} \leq e^{\beta[\rho/(1+\rho)]} \sum_y \Pr(\mathbf{y} \mid \mathbf{x}_m)^{1/1+\rho} \left[\sum_{\hat{m} \neq m} \Pr(\mathbf{y} \mid \mathbf{x}_{\hat{m}})^{1/1+\rho} \right]^\rho$$

$$= e^{\beta[\rho/(1+\rho)]} F_m, \qquad \rho \geq 0, \qquad \beta \geq 0; \tag{A.12}$$

$$P_{m\mathscr{E}} \leq e^{-\beta/[\rho(1+\rho)]} F_m, \qquad \rho \geq 0, \qquad \beta \geq 0, \tag{A.13}$$

where we have indicated that these bounds are the same, except for a multiplicative factor dependent on β.

Consider now the following method of choosing a code. Let

$$\mathbf{p} = \{p_j\} \tag{A.14a}$$

be any set of probabilities. To choose an input sequence to represent $\mathbf{x}_m$, let us choose N inputs independently from an ensemble in which the probability of choosing x_j is p_j. Over this ensemble,

$$\Pr[\mathbf{x}_m = (x_{j_1}, x_{j_2}, \cdots, x_{j_N})] = \prod_{i=1}^N p_{j_i}. \tag{A.14b}$$

Furthermore, let all code words be chosen in this way, independent of one another.

Equations A.12 and A.13 then apply to each word in the resulting code. Over the ensemble of all codes, we can define average values of P_{mx} and $P_{m\mathscr{E}}$, and bound them by

$$\overline{P_{mx}} \leq e^{\beta[\rho/(1+\rho)]} \overline{F}_m; \tag{A.15}$$

$$\overline{P_{m\mathscr{E}}} \leq e^{-\beta[\rho/(1+\rho)]} \overline{F}_m. \tag{A.16}$$

Finally, we bound $\overline{F}_m$:

$$\overline{F}_m = \overline{\sum_y \Pr(\mathbf{y} \mid \mathbf{x}_m)^{1/1+\rho} \left[\sum_{\hat{m} \neq m} \Pr(\mathbf{y} \mid \mathbf{x}_{\hat{m}})^{1/1+\rho} \right]^\rho} \tag{A.17}$$

$$= \sum_y \overline{\Pr(\mathbf{y} \mid \mathbf{x}_m)^{1/1+\rho} \left[\sum_{\hat{m} \neq m} \Pr(\mathbf{y} \mid \mathbf{x}_{\hat{m}})^{1/1+\rho} \right]^\rho} \tag{A.18}$$

$$= \sum_y \overline{\Pr(\mathbf{y} \mid \mathbf{x}_m)^{1/1+\rho}} \overline{\left[\sum_{\hat{m} \neq m} \Pr(\mathbf{y} \mid \mathbf{x}_{\hat{m}})^{1/1+\rho} \right]^\rho} \tag{A.19}$$

$$\leq \sum_y \overline{\Pr(\mathbf{y} \mid \mathbf{x}_m)^{1/1+\rho}} \left[\overline{\sum_{\hat{m} \neq m} \Pr(\mathbf{y} \mid \mathbf{x}_{\hat{m}})^{1/1+\rho}} \right]^\rho, \qquad \rho \leq 1 \tag{A.20}$$

$$= \sum_y \overline{\Pr(\mathbf{y} \mid \mathbf{x}_m)^{1/1+\rho}} \left[\sum_{\hat{m} \neq m} \overline{\Pr(\mathbf{y} \mid \mathbf{x}_{\hat{m}})^{1/1+\rho}} \right]^\rho \tag{A.21}$$

$$< \sum_{\mathbf{y}} \overline{\Pr(\mathbf{y} \mid \mathbf{x}_m)^{1/1+\rho}} M^\rho \overline{[\Pr(\mathbf{y} \mid \mathbf{x}_{\hat{m}})^{1/1+\rho}]}^\rho \qquad \text{(A.22)}$$

$$= e^{\rho NR} \sum_{\mathbf{y}} \overline{[\Pr(\mathbf{y} \mid \mathbf{x}_m)^{1/1+\rho}]}^{1+\rho} \qquad \text{(A.23)}$$

$$= e^{\rho NR} \sum_{\mathbf{y}} \overline{\left[\prod_{i=1}^{N} \Pr(y_i \mid x_{mi})^{1/1+\rho} \right]}^{1+\rho} \qquad \text{(A.24)}$$

$$= e^{\rho NR} \prod_{i=1}^{N} \sum_{k=1}^{K} \overline{\left[\Pr(y_i = y_k \mid x_{mi} = x_j)^{1/1+\rho} \right]}^{1+\rho} \qquad \text{(A.25)}$$

$$= \left\{ e^{\rho R} \sum_{k=1}^{K} \overline{\left[\Pr(y_k \mid x_j)^{1/1+\rho} \right]}^{1+\rho} \right\}^{N} \qquad \text{(A.26)}$$

$$= \left\{ e^{\rho R} \sum_{k=1}^{K} \left[\sum_{j=1}^{J} p_j p_{kj}^{1/1+\rho} \right]^{1+\rho} \right\}^{N}, \qquad \text{(A.27)}$$

where to go to Equation A.18 and to Equation A.21 we have used the fact that an average of a sum is the sum of the averages; to go to Equations A.19 and A.24 we have used that the average of a product of independent random variables is the product of the averages, independence being assured by our process of choosing a code; to go to Equation A.20 we have used that $\overline{f^\rho} \le \bar{f}^\rho$, $0 \le \rho \le 1$; to go to Equations A.22 and A.23 we have used that the total number of code words is $M = e^{NR}$; to go to Equation A.24 we have used Equation A.2; to go to Equation A.25 we have used the arithmetic rule for multiplying products of sums; to go to Equation A.26 we have used the memorylessness of the channel and the choosing process, expressed in Equations A.1 and A.14, to conclude that all terms are identical; and to go to Equation A.27 we have substituted Equation A.1 and written out the average indicated by the overbar. If we then define

$$E_0(\rho, \mathbf{p}) = -\ln \sum_{k=1}^{K} \left[\sum_{j=1}^{J} p_j p_{kj}^{1/1+\rho} \right]^{1+\rho}, \qquad \text{(A.28)}$$

we can summarize Equations A.17 through A.27 by

$$\bar{F}_m \le \exp\{-N[E_0(\rho, \mathbf{p}) - \rho R]\}, \qquad 0 \le \rho \le 1. \qquad \text{(A.29)}$$

Defining

$$E_{L0}(R) = \max_{\mathbf{p}, 0 \le \rho \le 1} [E_0(\rho, \mathbf{p}) - \rho R], \qquad \text{(A.30)}$$

and letting $\rho_0(R)$ be the ρ which maximizes Equation A.30, we have, substituting Equations A.29 and A.30 in Equations A.15 and A.16,

$$\overline{p_{mx}} \leq \exp\left[\beta \frac{\rho_0(R)}{1 + \rho_0(R)}\right] \exp\left[-NE_{L0}(R)\right]; \quad (A.31)$$

$$\overline{p_{m\mathscr{E}}} \leq \exp\left[-\beta \frac{\rho_0(R)}{1 + \rho_0(R)}\right] \exp\left[-NE_{L0}(R)\right]. \quad (A.32)$$

Since $\bar{F}_m \leq e^{-NE_{L0}(R)}$, there must be at least one code in the ensemble for which $F_m \leq e^{-NE_{L0}(R)}$; thus we have proved the following theorem.

THEOREM A.1 (Fano[2]-Gallager)

There exists a code of length N and rate R and an erasure strategy dependent on the criterion β such that the average error and erasure probabilities satisfy

$$\Pr(X) \leq K(\beta)e^{-NE_{L0}(R)} \quad (A.33)$$

$$\Pr(\mathscr{E}) \leq K^{-1}(\beta)e^{-NE_{L0}(R)}, \quad (A.34)$$

where, by proper choice of β, $K(\beta)$ may be made to assume any value not less than one.

At low rates this bound can be improved. For $\rho = 1$, Equations A.12 and A.13 become

$$p_{mx} \leq e^{\beta/2} \sum_{\mathbf{y}} \Pr(\mathbf{y} \mid \mathbf{x}_m)^{1/2} \sum_{\hat{m} \neq m} \Pr(\mathbf{y} \mid \mathbf{x}_{\hat{m}})^{1/2} \quad (A.35)$$

$$= e^{\beta/2} F_{1m};$$

$$p_{m\mathscr{E}} \leq e^{-\beta/2} F_{1m}, \quad (A.36)$$

where

$$F_{1m} = \sum_{\hat{m} \neq m} q(\mathbf{x}_m, \mathbf{x}_{\hat{m}}); \quad (A.37)$$

$$q(\mathbf{x}_m, \mathbf{x}_{\hat{m}}) = \sum_{\mathbf{y}} \sqrt{\Pr(\mathbf{y} \mid \mathbf{x}_m) \Pr(\mathbf{y} \mid \mathbf{x}_{\hat{m}})}. \quad (A.38)$$

Over the same ensemble of codes that we considered above, the probability that F_{1m} exceeds an arbitrary number B is given by

$$\Pr(F_{1m} \geq B) = \phi, \quad (A.39)$$

where

$$\phi = \begin{cases} 1, & F_{1m} \geq B; \\ 0, & \text{otherwise.} \end{cases} \quad (A.40)$$

From Equation A.37,

$$\phi \leq \sum_{\hat{m} \neq m} \left[\frac{q(\mathbf{x}_m, \mathbf{x}_{\hat{m}})}{B} \right], \tag{A.41}$$

and further

$$\phi \leq \sum_{\hat{m} \neq m} \left[\frac{q(\mathbf{x}_m, \mathbf{x}_{\hat{m}})}{B} \right]^{1/\rho}, \qquad 1 \leq \rho \leq \infty, \tag{A.42}$$

since, if $\phi = 1$, the sum in Equation A.41 either contains a term greater than 1, in which case Equation A.42 will also contain such a term, or it does not, in which case as ρ increases from 1 all terms increase. Then

$\Pr(F_{1m} \geq B)$

$$\leq B^{-1/\rho} \sum_{\hat{m} \neq m} \overline{q(\mathbf{x}_m, \mathbf{x}_{\hat{m}})^{1/\rho}} \tag{A.43}$$

$$= B^{-1/\rho} \sum_{\hat{m} \neq m} \overline{\left[\sum_{\mathbf{y}} \Pr(\mathbf{y} \mid \mathbf{x}_m)^{1/2} \Pr(\mathbf{y} \mid \mathbf{x}_{\hat{m}})^{1/2} \right]^{1/\rho}} \tag{A.44}$$

$$= B^{-1/\rho} \sum_{\hat{m} \neq m} \overline{\left[\prod_{i=1}^{N} \sum_{k=1}^{K} \Pr(y_i = y_k \mid x_{mi} = x_j)^{1/2} \Pr(y_i = y_k \mid x_{\hat{m}i} = x_j)^{1/2} \right]^{1/\rho}} \tag{A.45}$$

$$= B^{-1/\rho} \sum_{\hat{m} \neq m} \prod_{i=1}^{N} \overline{\left[\sum_{k=1}^{K} \Pr(y_i = y_k \mid x_{mi} = x_j)^{1/2} \Pr(y_i = y_k \mid x_{\hat{m}i} = x_j)^{1/2} \right]^{1/\rho}} \tag{A.46}$$

$$= B^{-1/\rho} \sum_{\hat{m} \neq m} \prod_{i=1}^{N} \sum_{j=1}^{J} \sum_{j'=1}^{J} p_j p_j \left(\sum_{k=1}^{K} p_{kj}^{1/2} p_{kj'}^{1/2} \right)^{1/\rho} \tag{A.47}$$

$$= B^{-1/\rho}(M-1) \left[\sum_{j=1}^{J} \sum_{j'=1}^{J} p_j p_j \left(\sum_{k=1}^{K} p_{kj}^{1/2} p_{kj'}^{1/2} \right)^{1/\rho} \right]^{N} \tag{A.48}$$

where to go to Equation A.45 we have successively substituted in Equations A.39, A.43, A.38, and A.2; to go to Equation A.46 we have used the fact that the average of a product of independent random variables is the product of their averages, independence being ensured by our choice of ensemble; to go to Equation A.47 we have written out the average indicated by the overbar; and to go to Equation A.48 we have used the fact that the term in square brackets in Equation A.48 is identical for all i and $\hat{m}$. Now let

$$E_x(\rho, \mathbf{p}) = -\rho \ln \sum_{j=1}^{J} \sum_{j'=1}^{J} p_j p_j \left(\sum_{k=1}^{K} p_{kj}^{1/2} p_{kj'}^{1/2} \right)^{1/\rho}, \tag{A.49}$$

and choose

$$B = [2(M - 1)]^{\rho} e^{-NE_x(\rho, \mathbf{p})}, \qquad (A.50)$$

so that, substituting Equation A.50 in Equation A.48,

$$\Pr(F_{1m} \geq B) \leq \tfrac{1}{2}. \qquad (A.51)$$

For each code in the ensemble of all codes, let us now eliminate all code words for which $F_{1m} \geq B$; by Equation A.51 the average number of code words eliminated will be not more than $M/2$, and thus there is at least one code left with $M/2$ words, which is to say rate

$$R = \frac{1}{N} \ln \frac{M}{2}.$$

All the words in this code have

$$F_{1m} < B < \exp \left\{ -N \left[E_x(\rho, \mathbf{p}) - \rho R - \frac{\rho \ln 4}{N} \right] \right\}, \qquad (A.52)$$

where we have used Equation A.50 and the fact that

$$M - 1 < 2e^{NR}.$$

Defining

$$E_{Lx}(R) = \max_{\mathbf{p}, \, 1 \leq \rho \leq \infty} [E_x(\rho, \mathbf{p}) - \rho R], \qquad (A.53)$$

and substituting Equation A.52 in Equations A.35 and A.36, we have proved the following theorem.

THEOREM A.2 (Gallager)

There exists a code of length N and rate R and an erasure strategy dependent on the criterion β such that the average error and erasure probabilities satisfy

$$\Pr(X) \leq K(\beta) \exp \{ -N[E_{Lx}(R) + o(1)] \};$$

$$\Pr(\mathscr{E}) \leq K^{-1}(\beta) \exp \{ -N[E_{Lx}(R) + o(1)] \},$$

where, by proper choice of β, $K(\beta)$ may be made to assume any value not less than one.

Theorems A.1 and A.2 give the lower-bound error exponent and a weak estimate of the tradeoff between erasure and error probabilities. The upper-bound exponent is given by the following theorems.

THEOREM A.3 (Fano-Gallager)

There exists no code of length N and rate R for which

$$\Pr(\mathscr{E}) \leq \exp \{ -N[E_{U0}(R) + o(1)] \},$$

where

$$E_{U0}(R) = \max_{\mathbf{p},\, 0 \le \rho \le \infty} [E_0(\rho, \mathbf{p}) - \rho R].$$

THEOREM A.4 (Berlekamp[1])

The greatest exponent E for which there exists a code of length N, with M code words, and with

$$\Pr(\mathscr{E}) \le e^{-NE}$$

for M and N arbitrarily large is

$$E = E_{Lx}(0).$$

COROLLARY

$$E(0) = E_U(0) = E_{Lx}(0).$$

THEOREM A.5 (Shannon-Gallager)

If the true exponent E(R) satisfies

$$E(R_1) \le E_1$$

and

$$E(R_2) \le E_{U0}(R_2),$$

where $R_1 < R_2$, then

$$E[\lambda R_1 + (1 - \lambda)R_2] \le \lambda E_1 + (1 - \lambda)E_{U0}(R_2), \qquad 0 \le \lambda \le 1.$$

COROLLARY

$$E(R) \le E_{sl}(R), \qquad 0 \le R \le R_{sl},$$

where $E_{sl}(R)$ is the tangent to $E_{U0}(R)$ which passes through $E_{Lx}(0)$, and R_{sl} is the point of tangency.

The properties of these exponents are discussed in more detail in Section 4.1.1.

References

1. E. R. Berlekamp, "Block Coding with Noiseless Feedback," Ph.D. thesis, Dept. of Electrical Engineering, Massachusetts Institute of Technology, Cambridge, Massachusetts, September, 1964.
2. R. M. Fano, *Transmission of Information*, M.I.T. Press and John Wiley & Sons, Inc., New York, 1961.
3. R. G. Gallager, "A Simple Derivation of the Coding Theorem and Some Applications," *IEEE Trans. Information Theory*, **IT-11**, 3–18 (1965).
4. R. G. Gallager, Private Communication (homework problem).
5. C. E. Shannon, R. G. Gallager, and E. R. Berlekamp, "Lower Bounds to Error Probability for Coding on Discrete Memoryless Channels," to be published.

Appendix B.   Decoding BCH Codes

Decoding of BCH codes is in general accomplished by an algorithm suitable for execution by a stored-program digital computer with an arithmetic unit capable of performing finite field operations. In this appendix we collect algorithms of this type and estimate the number of operations they require.

The appendix is divided into two sections. The first presents the basic erasure-and-error-correction algorithm, which is an extension of the error-correction algorithm of Gorenstein and Zierler.[4] This algorithm succeeds in finding the unique code word within the minimum distance of the received word, if there is one. We consider the complexity of implementation of this algorithm in a stored-program computer and find that the maximum number of operations required is proportional to d^3, or, for erasure-correction only, to d^2.

The second section collects a number of specialized algorithms, including some not appearing in Reference 3. These include a method of locating errors by the vanishing of a matrix determinant, alternate methods of computing error and erasure values, and a method of finding error locators which is particularly suitable for generalized minimum distance decoding. We expect, however, that the general reader will occupy himself only with the first section.

B.1   The Basic Algorithm

The code words **f** of a BCH code of length n and minimum distance

114

d on $GF(q')$ are all the words whose elements f_i are members of $GF(q')$ and satisfy

$$\sum_{i=1}^{n} f_i Z_i^m = 0, \qquad m_0 \leq m \leq m_0 + d - 2, \qquad (B.1)$$

where m_0 and d are arbitrary integers, and the Z_i, called locators, are distinct (and when $m_0 \neq 0$, nonzero) elements of some field $GF(q)$ which has $GF(q')$ as a subfield. (If 0 is a locator, we require use of the convention $0^0 = 1$.)

A received word $\mathbf{r}$ consists of n estimates r_i, which may also be considered elements of $GF(q')$. We shall consider that, when the detector signals an erasure, the decoder records the locator Y_k of the symbol erased as well as some estimate, perhaps arbitrary. If there are s erasures, the decoding problem is to find the code word closest to the received word, given the r_i, $1 \leq i \leq n$, and the Y_k, $1 \leq k \leq s$.

Let there be a word $\mathbf{f}$ satisfying Equation B.1 within the minimum distance of the received word; that is, one which differs from the received word in t unerased symbols, where

$$2t + s < d. \qquad (B.2)$$

Then, as we see in Chapter 3, there is only one such word. [If $\mathbf{f}$ has elements not in $GF(q')$, then it is not a code word, but this algorithm finds it anyway.] Let the locators corresponding to the places in which $\mathbf{r}$ and $\mathbf{f}$ differ be X_j, $1 \leq j \leq t$; we call these *error locators*, since, if $\mathbf{f}$ was the word actually transmitted, these will be the places in which symbol errors occurred. We define the *error value*

$$e_j = r_i - f_i, \qquad X_j = Z_i, \qquad 1 \leq j \leq t, \qquad (B.3a)$$

and similarly the *erasure value*

$$d_k = r_i - f_i, \qquad Y_k = Z_i, \qquad 1 \leq k \leq s; \qquad (B.3b)$$

these values are the differences in $GF(q)$ between the estimate and the corresponding symbol in $\mathbf{f}$. We note that $e_j \neq 0$. Now $\mathbf{f}$ may be determined from $\mathbf{r}$ and the values and locators of the erasures and errors by Equations B.3; thus the decoding problem reduces to finding the e_j, X_j, and d_k from the r_i and Y_k.

B.1.1   Syndromes. It is convenient to reduce the n estimates r_i to the $d - 1$ *syndromes* or parity checks S_m defined by

$$S_m = \sum_{i=1}^{n} r_i Z_i^m, \qquad m_0 \leq m \leq m_0 + d - 2. \qquad (B.4)$$

From Equations B.1 and B.3,

$$S_m = \sum_{j=1}^{t} e_j X_j^m + \sum_{k=1}^{s} d_k Y_k^m. \qquad (B.5)$$

The elementary symmetric functions σ_{dl} of the erasure locators Y_k are defined as the coefficients of the product

$$\prod_{k=1}^{s} (Z - Y_k) = \sum_{l=0}^{s} \sigma_{dl} Z^{s-l}; \qquad (B.6)$$

Thus

$$\sigma_{d0} = 1, \quad \sigma_{d1} = -\sum_{k=1}^{s} Y_k, \cdots, \sigma_{ds} = (-1)^s \prod_{k=1}^{s} Y_k.$$

Clearly, from Equation B.6

$$\sum_{l=0}^{s} \sigma_{dl} Z^{s-l} \begin{cases} = 0, & Z = Y_k, \text{ some } k; \\ \neq 0, & \text{otherwise}, \end{cases} \qquad (B.7)$$

since in a field a product of nonzero elements is nonzero. Now we define the *modified syndromes* as

$$T_n = \sum_{l=0}^{s} \sigma_{dl} S_{m_0 + n + s - l}, \qquad 0 \le n \le d - s - 2, \qquad (B.8)$$

where the restriction on n ensures that $m_0 \le m_0 + n + s - l \le m_0 + d - 2$. If $s = 0$, $T_n = S_{m_0 + n}$. Substituting Equation B.5 and using Equation B.7, we have

$$T_n = \sum_{l=0}^{s} \sigma_{dl} \sum_{j=1}^{t} e_j X_j^{m_0 + n + s - l} + \sum_{l=0}^{s} \sigma_{dl} \sum_{k=1}^{s} d_k Y_k^{m_0 + n + s - l}$$

$$= \sum_{j=1}^{t} e_j X_j^{m_0 + n} \sum_{l=0}^{s} \sigma_{dl} X_j^{s-l} + \sum_{k=1}^{s} d_k Y_k^{m_0 + n} \sum_{l=0}^{s} \sigma_{dl} Y_k^{s-l}$$

$$= \sum_{j=1}^{t} E_j X_j^n, \qquad (B.9)$$

where we have defined

$$E_j = e_j X_j^{m_0} \sum_{l=0}^{s} \sigma_{dl} X_j^{s-l}. \qquad (B.10)$$

Now E_j is nonzero, since e_j is nonzero, X_j is nonzero if $m_0 \neq 0$, and the sum is nonzero from Equation B.7 since $X_j \neq Y_k$.

B.1.2   Finding the Error Locators. In this section we show how to find the t error locators X_j from the $d - s - 1$ modified syndromes T_n.

Of course the decoder does not know t, but it may assume that $t \leq t_0$, where t_0 is the greatest integer such that $2t_0 + s < d$. For notational convenience we assume $e_j = X_j = 0$, $t + 1 \leq j \leq t_0$. Then Equation B.9 may be rewritten

$$T_n = \sum_{j=1}^{t_0} E_j X_j^n \qquad 0 \leq n \leq d - s - 2, \qquad (B.11)$$

where $E_j \neq 0$, $1 \leq j \leq t$; $E_j = 0$, $t + 1 \leq j \leq t_0$.

We find it convenient to solve not for the X_j but for the elementary symmetric functions $\sigma_{el'}$ of the X_j, defined by

$$\prod_{j=1}^{t_0} (Z - X_j) = \sum_{l'=0}^{t_0} \sigma_{el'} Z^{t_0 - l'} \begin{cases} = 0, & Z = X_j; \\ \neq 0, & Z \neq X_j. \end{cases} \qquad (B.12)$$

Again $\sigma_{e0} = 1$; also $\sigma_{el'} = 0$, $t + 1 \leq l' \leq t_0$. We have from Equations B.11 and B.12

$$\sum_{l'=0}^{t_0} \sigma_{el'} T_{n' + t_0 - l'} = \sum_{j=1}^{t_0} E_j X_j^{n'} \sum_{l'=0}^{t_0} \sigma_{el'} X_j^{t_0 - l'} = 0,$$

$$0 \leq n' \leq t_0 - 1, \quad (B.13)$$

where the restriction on n' ensures that $0 \leq n' + t_0 - l' \leq 2t_0 - 1 \leq d - s - 2$, since $2t_0 \leq d - s - 1$. From Equation B.13 and the fact that $\sigma_{e0} = 1$, we have the t_0 equations

$$\sum_{l'=1}^{t_0} \sigma_{el'} T_{n' + t_0 - l'} = -T_{n' + t_0}, \qquad 0 \leq n' \leq t_0 - 1, \qquad (B.14)$$

in the t_0 unknowns $\sigma_{el'}$, $1 \leq l' \leq t_0$.

The coefficient matrix $\{T_{n' + t_0 - l'}\}$ determines the solubility of these equations. Its important properties are derived from a factorization into three matrices A, B, and C which is due to Gorenstein and Zierler.[4] Let A be the van der Monde matrix with elements

$$A_{n'j} = X_j^{n'}, \qquad 1 \leq j \leq t_0, \qquad 0 \leq n' \leq t_0 - 1; \qquad (B.15)$$

B, the diagonal matrix with elements

$$B_{jj'} = E_j \delta_{jj'}, \qquad 1 \leq j \leq t_0, \qquad 1 \leq j' \leq t_0, \qquad (B.16)$$

where $\delta_{jj'}$ is the Kronecker delta; and C, the van der Monde matrix with elements

$$C_{jl'} = X_{j'}^{t_0 - l'}, \qquad 1 \leq l' \leq t_0, \qquad 1 \leq j' \leq t_0. \qquad (B.17)$$

Then,

$$\sum_{j=1}^{t_0} \sum_{j'=1}^{t_0} A_{n'j} B_{jj'} C_{j'l'} = \sum_{j=1}^{t_0} E_j X_j^{n'+t_0-l'} = T_{n'+t_0-l'}, \qquad (B.18)$$

so that the coefficient matrix is indeed the product of A, B, and C. But A and C are van der Monde, with at least t different locators X_j, and so have rank at least t (see Chapter 2), while B is diagonal with t nonzero diagonal elements (from Equation B.11), and so has rank exactly t. Therefore the rank of $\{T_{n'+t_0-l'}\}$ is t. Determining this rank informs the decoder that $\sigma_{el'} = 0$, $t+1 \le l' \le t_0$.

We then have from Equation B.14 the t equations in t unknowns

$$\sum_{l'=1}^{t} \sigma_{el'} T_{n'+t_0-l'} = -T_{n'+t_0}, \qquad 0 \le n' \le t-1. \qquad (B.14a)$$

The coefficient matrix in these equations is the product

$$T_{n'+t_0-l'} = \sum_{j=1}^{t} \sum_{j'=1}^{t} (X_j^{n'})(E_j \delta_{jj'})(X_{j'}^{t_0-l'}). \qquad (B.19)$$

$\{X_j^{n'}\}$ and $\{E_j \delta_{jj'}\}$ have rank t, as just shown; $\{X_{j'}^{t_0-l'}\}$ has rank t if $t = t_0$ or if $X_j \ne 0$, all j, otherwise rank $t-1$. Thus $\{T_{n'+t_0-l'}\}$ has rank t unless $t \ne t_0$ and some $X_j = 0$. Either we can invert it and solve for the $\sigma_{el'}$, or we cannot; in the latter case we set $X_t = 0$, $\sigma_{et} = 0$, and solve the equations

$$\sum_{l'=0}^{t-1} \sigma_{el'} T_{n'+t_0-l'} = -T_{n'+t_0}, \qquad 0 \le n' \le t-2, \qquad (B.14b)$$

to get the $\sigma_{el'}$, $1 \le l' \le t-1$.

Having obtained the $\sigma_{el'}$, the decoder can compute Equation B.12 for each of the locators to find which are the error locators.

B.1.3   Determining Error and Erasure Values. At this point the remaining problem is to find the error and erasure values, given the error and erasure locators. To simplify notation, we do not distinguish between errors and erasures, but simply consider the problem of finding s erasure values d_k, $1 \le k \le s$, given their locators Y_k and the syndromes S_m, $m_0 \le m \le m_0 + d - 2$.

In this case, Equation B.5 becomes

$$S_m = \sum_{k=1}^{s} d_k Y_k^m, \qquad m_0 \le m \le m_0 + d - 2. \qquad (B.5a)$$

Define the elementary symmetric functions $\sigma_{k'l}$ of the erasure locators save $Y_{k'}$ by

$$\prod_{k \neq k'} (Z - Y_k) = \sum_{l=0}^{s-1} \sigma_{k'l} Z^{s-1-l}; \qquad (\text{B.20})$$

comparing Equation B.6 with B.20, we have

$$(Z - Y_{k'}) \sum_{l=0}^{s-1} \sigma_{k'l} Z^{s-1-l} = \sum_{l=0}^{s} \sigma_{dl} Z^{s-l}, \qquad (\text{B.21})$$

from which, equating coefficients, we get

$$\sigma_{dl} = \sigma_{k'l} - Y_{k'} \sigma_{k'(l-1)}. \qquad (\text{B.22})$$

Equation B.22 allows recursive determination of the $\sigma_{k'l}$ from the σ_{dl}.

From Equations B.5a and B.20, we have

$$\sum_{l=0}^{s-1} \sigma_{k'l} S_{m_0+s-1-l} = \sum_{k=1}^{s} d_k Y_k^{m_0} \sum_{l=0}^{s-1} \sigma_{k'l} Y_k^{s-1-l}$$

$$= d_{k'} Y_{k'}^{m_0} \sum_{l=0}^{s-1} \sigma_{k'l} Y_{k'}^{s-1-l}, \qquad (\text{B.23})$$

so that

$$d_{k'} = \frac{\displaystyle\sum_{l=0}^{s-1} \sigma_{k'l} S_{m_0+s-1-l}}{\displaystyle\sum_{l=0}^{s-1} \sigma_{k'l} Y_{k'}^{m_0+s-1-l}}. \qquad (\text{B.24})$$

From Equation B.24 we can determine all erasure values $d_{k'}$.

This completes the basic algorithm.

B.1.4 Complexity of Implementation. The preceding algorithm is generally applicable to any BCH code. To simplify some parts of the decoding, we shall assume now that the code is of length q and cyclic-plus—that is, cyclic with an over-all parity check—so that $m_0 = 0$, $Z_0 = 0$, and $Z_i = \alpha^i$, $1 \leq i \leq q - 1$, where α is a primitive element of $GF(q)$. The other codes of practical interest are the cyclic codes with $m_0 = 1$, which are subsumed by the cyclic-plus codes (see Section 2.3.1). Furthermore, because computers are most easily constructed with bistable memory elements, we shall assume that the locator field $GF(q)$ has characteristic two, so that $q = 2^M$ for some M, and that, if the code is not Reed-Solomon, all estimates r_i are converted to their representations in the locator field. A finite field element is then represented by M bits.

We shall estimate the number of operations required to execute the basic algorithm by a stored-program computer with a finite field arithmetic unit. Such a unit must at least be able to add, multiply, or invert elements of $GF(q)$. Since the field has characteristic two, subtraction is realized by addition; division is realized by multiplication of the dividend by the inverse of the divisor. It is also convenient to have the capability to multiply by α^m, $1 \leq m \leq d - 2$. Peterson[6] and Bartee and Schneider[1] have considered how to realize these functions; they have shown that multiplication and inversion, the two most difficult operations, can be accomplished either in parallel, by a single combinational circuit, or serially, by a number of elementary operations (adds and shifts) proportional to $M = \log_2 q$. As all registers are M bits long, the hardware complexity of the arithmetic unit is proportional to no more than $(\log_2 q)^2$.

The two other contributors to complexity are the number of operations required and the number of memory registers, which we now proceed to estimate.

Storage of the r_i and the Y_k requires $q + s$ memory registers.

Calculation of the syndromes is facilitated if the symbols are received in reverse order, so that $Z_i = \alpha^{-i}$, $1 \leq i \leq q - 1$, and $Z_q = 0$. Then the iteration

$$S_m = [(r_1 \alpha^m + r_2)\alpha^m + r_3]\alpha^m + r_4 \cdots$$

realizes Equation B.4 for $m \neq 0$, if r_q is omitted. Also

$$S_0 = \sum_{i=1}^{q} r_i.$$

$(q - 1)$ multiplications by α^m are required; storage of the results requires $d - 1$ memory registers.

The elementary symmetric functions of the erasure locators σ_{dl} can be computed recursively from Equation B.22, in a number of multiplications proportional to s^2, and stored in s memory registers.

The modified syndromes can then be computed from Equation B.8 with $s(d - s - 1)$ multiplications, and stored in $d - s - 1$ memory registers.

Equations B.14 can be set up in $t_0(t_0 + 1)$ memory registers; a Gauss-Jordan reduction to upper triangular form will not only determine the rank t but also leave either Equations B.14a or B.14b in upper triangular form, so that the σ_{el} can be readily determined. This is the most lengthy single step in the calculation, since a Gauss-Jordan reduction requires a number of multiplications proportional to t_0^3.

Evaluation of Equation B.12 for Z equal to each of the nonzero locators is most easily accomplished by the method of Chien.[2] If

$$\sum_{l'=0}^{t_0} \sigma_{el'} = 0,$$

then 1 is an error locator. Let $\sigma'_{el'} = \alpha^{t_0-l'}\sigma'_{el'}$; then if

$$\sum_{l'=0}^{t_0} \sigma'_{el'} = 0,$$

α is an error locator. The $(q - 1)$ iterations of this procedure will determine in turn whether each of the nonzero elements of $GF(q)$ is an error locator. t memory registers are required for storage of the error locators.

Finally, to find the values of the erasures and errors, we first fold the error locators just found into the σ_{dl}, then determine the elementary symmetric functions $\sigma_{k'l}$ from the σ_{dl} by Equation B.22, which requires $(s + t)^2$ operations to get all $(s + t)^2$ of them. The use of Equation B.24 to find all error and erasure values involves a number of operations proportional to $(s + t)^2$.

In summary, the maximum number of computations is proportional only to $t_0^3 \sim d^3$, and the number of memory registers only to $t_0^2 \sim d^2$. For erasure-correction only, the maximum number of operations is proportional only to $s^2 \sim d^2$.

B.2 Modifications of the Basic Algorithm

In this section we present briefly some additional relationships which provide alternate methods of executing steps of the basic algorithm. Some are of theoretical interest only; others may have specialized practical application.

RELATIONSHIP 1

The matrix D whose elements are

$$D_{n'l'} = T_{n'+t-l'}, \qquad 0 \le l' \le t, \qquad 0 \le n' \le t - 1;$$
$$D_{tl'} = Z^{t-l'}, \qquad 0 \le l' \le t, \qquad \qquad \text{(B.25)}$$

has zero determinant if and only if Z equals an error locator X_j.

Proof:

Suppose $Z = X_j$. Then, from Equation B.12 and analogously to Equation B.13,

$$\sum_{l'=0}^{t} \sigma_{el'} T_{n'+t-l'} = 0, \qquad 0 \le n' \le t - 1;$$

$$\sum_{l'=0}^{t} \sigma_{el'} X_j^{t-l'} = 0,$$

so that $\sigma_{el'}$ is a nonzero vector which when multiplied into D gives zero; there must then be linear dependence between rows of D, and thus $|D| = 0$. Conversely, suppose $|D| = 0$; then there is some vector $\mathbf{a} = \{a_{l'}\}$ such that $\mathbf{a}D = 0$. Since the first t rows $(0 \leq n' \leq t - 1)$ of D are linearly independent by arguments similar to those of Section B.1.2, the set of vectors $\mathbf{a}$ which satisfy

$$\sum_{l'=0}^{t} a_{l'} T_{n'+t-l'} = 0$$

consists of a single vector $\mathbf{a}_0$ multiplied by any constant factor b. But $\boldsymbol{\sigma}_e$ is such a vector; therefore, $\mathbf{a} = b\boldsymbol{\sigma}_e$. Now for $\mathbf{a}D = 0$, we must have

$$\sum_{l'=0}^{t} b\sigma_{el'} Z^{t-l'} = 0;$$

but this is true only if Z is an error locator X_j.

Comments: By this relationship we can determine the error locators directly from the modified syndromes T_n. This does not represent a simplification within a stored-program computer structure, for to evaluate the determinant $|D|$ involves calculation of the $t + 1$ minors of the last row; at approximately t^3 calculations for each minor, the total number of calculations is proportional to t^4. Rather, this relationship might form the nucleus of a decoder made up simply of digital circuitry; it suggests a giant combinational circuit with $t_0 + 1$ M-bit inputs (the t_0, T_n, and Z) and a single output indicating whether the determinant was zero or not. The error-forcing technique of Massey[5] would be used to ensure $t = t_0$. Besides the difficulty of constructing such a circuit, one would have to face the problems of generating the modified syndromes from the received word and solving for the error and erasure values. This is the nonbinary generalization of the "direct method" of Chien.[2]

RELATIONSHIP 2

$$d_{k'} = \frac{\displaystyle\sum_{l'=0}^{s-1} \sigma_{dl'} Y_{k'}^{-l'} U_{l'}}{\displaystyle\sum_{l'=0}^{s-1} (s-l')\sigma_{dl'} Y_{k'}^{m_0+s-1-l'}}, \qquad (B.26)$$

where

$$U_{l'} = \sum_{l=l'}^{s-1} S_{m_0+s-1-l} Y_{k'}^{l}. \qquad (B.27)$$

Proof:

Solving Equation B.22 recursively, we obtain

$$\sigma_{k'l} = \sum_{l'=0}^{l} \sigma_{dl'} Y_{k'}^{l-l'} \tag{B.28}$$

Substituting Equation B.28 in Equation B.24, we obtain Equations B.26 and B.27.

Comments: If the powers of $Y_{k'}$ are easily obtained, Equation B.26 may be simpler to calculate than Equation B.24. Note that in a field of characteristic two, half the terms in the denominator (those for which $s - l' = 0 \bmod 2$) vanish.

RELATIONSHIP 3

$$e_j = \frac{\displaystyle\sum_{l=0}^{t-1} \sigma_{j'l} T_{t-1-l}}{X_{j'0}^{m} \left[\displaystyle\sum_{l=0}^{t-1} \sigma_{j'l} X_{j'}^{t-1-l} \right]\left[\displaystyle\sum_{l=0}^{s} \sigma_{dl} X_{j'}^{s-l} \right]} \tag{B.29}$$

where the elementary symmetric functions $\sigma_{j'l}$ are defined by

$$\prod_{j \neq j'}(Z - X_j) = \sum_{l=0}^{t-1} \sigma_{j'l} Z^{t-1-l}. \tag{B.30}$$

Proof:

From Equation B.9

$$\sum_{l=0}^{t-1} \sigma_{j'l} T_{t-1-l} = \sum_{j=1}^{t} E_j \sum_{l=0}^{t-1} \sigma_{j'l} X_j^{t-1-l}$$

$$= E_{j'} \sum_{l=0}^{t-1} \sigma_{j'l} X_{j'}^{t-1-l}, \tag{B.31}$$

with use of Equation B.30. Substituting Equation B.10 in Equation B.31 and solving for $e_{j'}$, we get Equation B.29.

Comments: Equation B.29 is a rewriting of Equation B.24; it will require slightly less calculation to find the $\sigma_{j'l}$ than the $\sigma_{k'l}$. Relationship 2 may also be applied to Equation B.29.

RELATIONSHIP 4

$$e_{j'} = \frac{|M_{t*}|}{X_{j'0}^{m+t_0-t*} \left[\displaystyle\sum_{l=0}^{s} \sigma_{dl} X_{j'}^{s-l} \right]\left[\displaystyle\sum_{n'=0}^{t*-1} |M_{n'}| X_{j'}^{2n'} \right]} \tag{B.32}$$

where $t^* = t - 1$ if one of the X_j equals zero and $t \neq t_0$; otherwise $t^* = t$; $|M_{t^*}|$ is the determinant of the matrix with elements

$$T_{n'+t_0-l'}, \qquad 0 \leq n' \leq t^* - 1, \qquad 1 \leq l' \leq t^*, \qquad \text{(B.33)}$$

$|M_{n'}|$ is the determinant of the matrix remaining when the row indexed by n' and the column indexed by $t^* - n'$ are struck from the matrix of Equation B.33, and the locator field has characteristic two.

Proof:

From the discussion under Equation B.19, we know that M_{t^*} has rank t^*, and therefore $|M_{t^*}| \neq 0$. Let M'_{t^*} have elements

$$T_{n'+t_0-l'} - E_j X_{j'}^{n'+t_0-l'}; \qquad \text{(B.34)}$$

then by the same arguments $|M'_{t^*}| = 0$. The determinant of a $t^* \times t^*$ matrix with elements $a_{n'l'} + b_{n'l'}$ is the sum of the 2^{t^*} determinants whose elements are

$$a_{n'l'}, \qquad n' \in A;$$
$$b_{n'l'}, \qquad n' \in B,$$

where A and B are any of the 2^{t^*} divisions of the integers from 0 to $t^* - 1$ into two distinct sets. In this case, with $a_{n'l'} = T_{n'+t_0-l'}$ and $b_{n'l'} = -E_j X_{j'}^{n'+t_0-l'}$, the determinant corresponding to the case in which B is empty is $|M_{t^*}|$; the determinant corresponding to the case in which B has a single member n'_0 is

$$-E_j \sum_{l'=1}^{t} |M_{n_0 l'}| X_{j'}^{n_0'+t_0-l'}$$

where $M_{n_0 l'}$ is the determinant of the matrix remaining when the n'_0th row and l'th column are struck from M_{t^*}, and we have expanded in terms of the minors of the n'_0th row. When B has two or more members, two or more rows of the resulting matrix are simply a power of $X_{j'}$ times one another, so all other determinants are zero. It follows that

$$0 = |M'_{t^*}| = |M_{t^*}| - E_j \sum_{n'=0}^{t^*-1} \sum_{l'=1}^{t} |M_{n'l'}| X_{j'}^{n'+t_0-l'}. \qquad \text{(B.35)}$$

By symmetry, $|M_{n'l'}| = |M_{t^*-l', t^*-n'}|$; in a field of characteristic two, where $\beta + \beta = 0$, all but a few terms in the sum of Equation B.35 cancel, giving

$$0 = |M_{t^*}| - E_j \sum_{n'=0}^{t-1} |M_{n', t^*-n'}| X_{j'}^{2n'+t_0-t^*}. \qquad \text{(B.36)}$$

Substitution of Equation B.10 in Equation B.36 and solution for $e_{j'}$ gives the required relationship.

Comments: $|M_{t^*}|$ is easily obtained as a byproduct of the Gauss-Jordan reduction of Equation B.14; if t^* is small, it may be easier to use this relationship than one of our others for computing error values. Elsewhere[3] we have discussed the simultaneous calculation of all $|M_{n'}|$.

B.3 An Algorithm for GMD Decoding

Generalized minimum distance decoding of a BCH code involves a series of trials. For the purposes of this section we shall let the first trial be that for which the $d - 1$ least reliable symbols are erased; since any $d - 1$ places are a check set in an RS code (compare Section 2.3), the first trial always results in a word of the RS code from which the BCH code was derived. The second trial will be that for which the $d - 3$ least reliable symbols are erased, the third $d - 5$, and so forth.

One would think that some use could be made of the results of previous trials to simplify decoding. This section reports an algorithm which, in some cases, does require less computation.

With $d - 1 - 2t$ erasures, the maximum number of errors that can be corrected is t. Call the set of unerased places S_t; if the tth trial succeeds, the resulting code word C_t differs from the received word R in no more than t of the places in S_t. For the $(t + 1)$st trial, two symbols which were erased on the tth trial are restored. Suppose that the $(t + 1)$st trial results in a code word C_{t+1} which is not the same as C_t; then C_{t+1} must differ from R in $t + 1$ places of S_t and therefore equal R in the two symbols just restored, while C_t must differ from R in t places of S_t as well as in the two restored symbols so as to differ in $t + 2$ places in all. It follows that the code word $(C_t - C_{t+1})$ is a word with no more than $t + 1 + t + 2$ nonzero elements in S_{t+1} or, since the complementary set $\bar{S}_{t+1}$ contains $d - 1 - 2(t + 1)$ erased places, no more than d nonzero elements in all. But then it must have weight d, and the places in S_{t+1} in which C_t differs from R and those in which C_{t+1} differs from R are distinct.

From these considerations, we see the desirability of an algorithm which can find a code word $(C_t - C_{t+1})$ with $2t + 3$ nonzero elements in a set of places S_{t+1}, where the complementary erased set $\bar{S}_{t+1}$ is of size $d - 2t - 3$, when one knows $t + 2$ of the nonzero symbols $(C_t - R)$; the unknowns are the location and values of the $t + 1$ nonzero symbols in $(C_{t+1} - R)$. We give in Section B.3.1 an algorithm which finds these unknowns in a number of operations proportional to $(t + 1)^2$. Since the first trial involves erasure-correction only, and therefore $(d - 1)^2$ operations, the total number of operations required for GMD decoding is proportional to d^3 just as with errors-only or erasures-and-errors decoding, if a code word is found at every trial.

The catch is that some of the trials may fail to produce a code word. Suppose that, after the tth trial results in C_t, the next e trials fail. On the $(t + e + 1)$st trial, the maximum number of places in which C_t can differ from R in S_{t+e+1} is $t + 2e + 2$. We want on this trial to find a code word C_{t+e+1} which differs from R in S_{t+e+1} in $t + e + 1$ places, or equivalently to find a code word $(C_t - C_{t+e+1})$ which is distance $t + e + 1$ from $(C_t - R)$ in S_{t+e+1}, where $(C_t - R)$ may have as many as $t + 2e + 2$ nonzero elements. The algorithm in Section B.3.1 requires a number of operations proportional to $e^2(t + e + 1) + (t + e + 1)^2$ to solve this problem. For small e, it is therefore still probably simpler than the basic algorithm; however, as e approaches its maximum value of $(d - 3)/2$ (on the last trial when none has succeeded since the first), the new algorithm is undoubtedly more complicated.

B.3.1   The Algorithm. Let $Y_{k'}$, $1 \le k' \le s$, be a set $\bar{S}_t$ of s erasure locators, where $s = d - 1 - 2t$. Let W be a word with $t + 1 + e$ nonzero elements in the complementary set of places S_t, with Z_k being the locators of these nonzero symbols and r_k their values, $1 \le k \le t + 1 + e$. Let C be a code word which differs from W in t places in S_t, so that $E = C - W$ has t nonzero values e_j in the places with locators X_j, $1 \le j \le t$. Let the values of C in $\bar{S}_t$ be $d_{k'}$, $1 \le k' \le s$.

Since $C = W + E$ is a code word, its syndromes S_m are zero:

$$S_m = \sum_{j=1}^{t} e_j X_j^m + \sum_{k'=1}^{s} d_{k'} Y_{k'}^m + \sum_{k=1}^{t+1+e} r_k Z_k^m = 0,$$

$$m_0 \le m \le m_0 + d - 2. \quad (B.37)$$

With use of the elementary symmetric functions σ_{dl} of the erasure locators $Y_{k'}$, defined in Equation B.6, we have the modified syndromes

$$T_n = \sum_{l=0}^{s} \sigma_{dl} S_{m_0 + n + s - l}$$

$$= \sum_{j=1}^{t} E_j X_j^n + \sum_{k=1}^{t+1+e} R_k Z_k^n = 0, \qquad 0 \le n \le 2t - 1, \quad (B.38)$$

where we have defined

$$E_j = e_j X_j^{m_0} \sum_{l=0}^{s} \sigma_{dl} X_j^{s-l};$$

$$R_k = r_k Z_k^{m_0} \sum_{l=0}^{s} \sigma_{dl} Z_k^{s-l}. \quad (B.39)$$

Using Equation B.39, we can also define the modified syndromes

$$T_n = \sum_{j=1}^{t} E_j X_j^n + \sum_{k=1}^{t+1+e} R_k Z_k^n, \qquad 2t \le n \le 2t + e, \qquad (B.40)$$

which are not zero, as in Equation B.38, but unknown. Using the elementary symmetric functions σ_{el} of the X_j defined by Equation B.12, and the elementary symmetric functions $\sigma_{k'l'}$ of the X_j and Z_k save $Z_{k'}$, defined by

$$\prod_{j=1}^{t} (Z - X_j) \prod_{k \ne k'} (Z - Z_k) = \sum_{l'=0}^{2t+e} \sigma_{k'l'} Z^{2t+e-l'}, \qquad (B.41)$$

we have the $t + e + 1$ equations

$$\sum_{l'=0}^{2t+e} \sigma_{k'l'} T_{2t+e-l'} = R_{k'} \sum_{l'=0}^{2t+e} \sigma_{k'l'} Z_{k'}^{2t+e-l'}$$

$$= R_{k'} \prod_{j=1}^{t} (Z_{k'} - X_j) \prod_{k \ne k'} (Z_{k'} - Z_k)$$

$$= P_{k'}^{-1} \sum_{l=0}^{t} \sigma_{el} Z_{k'}^{t-l}, \qquad 1 \le k' \le t + e + 1,$$

$$(B.42)$$

where we have defined

$$P_{k'} = \left[R_{k'} \prod_{k \ne k'} (Z_{k'} - Z_k) \right]^{-1}. \qquad (B.43)$$

If we define the elementary symmetric functions σ_{ri} by

$$\prod_{j=1}^{t} (Z - X_j) \prod_{k=1}^{t+e+1} (Z - Z_k) = \sum_{i=0}^{2t+e+1} \sigma_{ri} Z^{2t+e+1-i}, \qquad (B.44)$$

then, from Equation B.28

$$\sigma_{k'l'} = \sum_{i=0}^{l'} \sigma_{ri} Z_{k'}^{l'-i} = \sum_{i'=0}^{l'} \sigma_{r(l'-i')} Z_{k'}^{i'}; \qquad (B.45)$$

substituting Equation B.45 in B.42, we obtain

$$\sum_{l=0}^{t} \sigma_{el} Z_{k'}^{t-l} = P_{k'} \sum_{l'=0}^{2t+e} T_{2t+e-l'} \sum_{i'=0}^{l'} \sigma_{r(l'-i')} Z_{k'}^{i'}$$

$$= P_{k'} \sum_{l'=0}^{e} T_{2t+e-l'} \sum_{i'=0}^{l'} \sigma_{r(l'-i')} Z_{k'}^{i'}$$

$$= P_{k'} \sum_{i'=0}^{e} Z_{k'}^{i'} \sum_{l'=i'}^{e} \sigma_{r(l'-i')} T_{2t+e-l'}$$

$$= P_{k'} \sum_{i'=0}^{e} a_{i'} Z_{k'}^{i'}, \qquad 1 \le k' \le t + e + 1, \qquad (B.46)$$

where we have used $T_n = 0$, $n \leq 2t - 1$, and defined

$$a_{i'} = \sum_{l'=i'}^{e} \sigma_{r(l'-i')}T_{2t+e-l'}. \tag{B.47}$$

Equations B.46 are $t + e + 1$ equations in $t + e + 1$ unknowns, namely the $e + 1$ a_i and the t σ_{el} (σ_{e0} being 1 always); the latter are the unknowns of interest, since from them we can determine the error locators X_j and thence the error values by the techniques of the basic algorithm.

We require one more manipulation. Consider the van der Monde matrix with elements

$$Z_k^j, \quad 1 \leq k \leq t + e + 1, \quad 0 \leq j \leq t + e. \tag{B.48}$$

If $\sigma_{k'j'}$ is defined by

$$\prod_{k \neq k'} (Z - Z_k) = \sum_{j'=0}^{t+e} \sigma_{k'(t+e-j')}Z^{j'} \tag{B.49}$$

and $Q_{k'}$ by

$$Q_{k'}^{-1} = \sum_{j'=0}^{t+e} \sigma_{k'(t+e-j')}Z_{k'}^{j'} = \prod_{k \neq k'} (Z_{k'} - Z_k), \tag{B.50}$$

then the right-hand inverse of $\{Z_k^j\}$ is $\{\sigma_{k'(t+e-j)}Q_{k'}\}$, since

$$\sum_{j=0}^{t+e} Z_k^j \sigma_{k'(t+e-j)}Q_{k'} = \delta_{kk'}, \tag{B.51}$$

by Equations B.25 and B.26, where $\delta_{kk'}$ is the Kronecker delta. But $\{Z_k^j\}$ is van der Monde with distinct rows, is therefore nonsingular, and must then have its left-hand inverse equal to its right, so that

$$\sum_{k=1}^{t+e+1} Z_k^j \sigma_{k(t+e-j')}Q_k = \delta_{jj'}. \tag{B.52}$$

Applying Equation B.52 to Equation B.46, we obtain

$$\sum_{i'=0}^{e} a_{i'} \sum_{k'=1}^{t+e+1} P_{k'}Z_{k'}^{i'}Q_{k'}\sigma_{k'(t+e-j)} = \sum_{l=0}^{t} \sigma_{el} \sum_{k'=1}^{t+e+1} Z_{k'}^{t-l}Q_{k'}\sigma_{k'(t+e-j)}$$

$$= \begin{cases} \sigma_{e(t-j)}, & 0 \leq j \leq t; \\ 0, & t+1 \leq j \leq t+e. \end{cases} \tag{B.53}$$

If $e = 0$, Equation B.53 becomes

$$\sum_{k'=1}^{t+1} P_{k'}Q_{k'}\sigma_{k'(t-j)} = a_0^{-1}\sigma_{e(t-j)}, \quad 0 \leq j \leq t; \tag{B.53a}$$

where $P_{k'}$, $Q_{k'}$, and $\sigma_{k'(t-j)}$ are given by Equations B.43, B.49, and B.50. Calculation of the left-hand side of Equation B.53a can be done in a number of operations proportional to t^2; then the error locators are the roots of

$$\sum_{j=0}^{t} a_0^{-1}\sigma_{e(t-j)}Z^j, \tag{B.54}$$

whose roots are obviously identical to those of Equation B.12. This is simpler than the Gauss-Jordan reduction by which the basic algorithm finds the σ_{el}; the remaining steps of the algorithm are the same.

If $e > 0$, the $a_{i'}$ can be determined in terms of a_0 by solution of the last e equations of Equation B.53:

$$-a_0 \sum_{k'=1}^{t+e+1} P_{k'}Q_{k'}\sigma_{k'(t+e-j)} = \sum_{i'=1}^{e} a_{i'} \sum_{k'=1}^{t+e+1} P_{k'}Z_{k'}^{i'}Q_{k'}\sigma_{k'(t+e-j)},$$

$$t+1 \leq j \leq t+e; \tag{B.55}$$

then the σ_{el} can be determined to within the constant of proportionality a_0 as before. An efficient procedure is a Gauss-Jordan-like reduction of the matrix

$$\left\{ \sum_{k'=1}^{t+e+1} P_{k'}Z_{k'}^{i'}Q_{k'}\sigma_{k'(t+e-j)} \right\}, \qquad 0 \leq j \leq t+e, \qquad 0 \leq i' \leq e$$

to a matrix $a_{ji'}$ in which $a_{ji'} = 0$, $0 \leq j \leq t$, $i' \neq 0$, whose first column ($i' = 0$) will then give the desired $\sigma_{e(t-j)}$; such a reduction requires a number of operations proportional to $e^2(t+e)$. Thus, when e approaches t, this method becomes at least as complicated as the basic algorithm and undoubtedly in practice more so.

References

1. T. C. Bartee and D. I. Schneider, "Computation with Finite Fields," *Information and Control*, **6**, 79–98 (1963).
2. R. T. Chien, "Cyclic Decoding Procedures for Bose-Chaudhuri-Hocquenghem Codes," *IEEE Trans. Information Theory*, **IT-10**, 357–363 (1964).
3. G. D. Forney, Jr., "On Decoding BCH Codes," *IEEE Trans. Information Theory*, **IT-11**, 549–557 (1965).
4. D. Gorenstein and N. Zierler, "A Class of Cyclic Linear Error-Correcting Codes in p^m Symbols," *J. Soc. Indust. Appl. Math.*, **9**, 207–214 (1961).
5. J. L. Massey, "Step-by-Step Decoding of the Bose-Chaudhuri-Hocquenghem Codes," *IEEE Trans. Information Theory*, **IT-11**, 580–585 (1965).
6. W. W. Peterson, *Error-Correcting Codes*, M.I.T. Press and John Wiley & Sons, Inc., New York, 1961, Section 7.3.

Appendix C. Performance of List Decoding

List decoding, as we defined it in Chapter 3, is a generalization of GMD decoding. In this appendix we show that, under certain restrictions necessary for a GMD-type treatment, no improvement in performance results from the generalization to lists, to the accuracy of a Chernov bound.

We assume that on each use of the channel one of J inputs x_j is transmitted and at the receiver a list detector produces from the output y a list of J numbers $\{\alpha_j(y)\}$. A received word $\boldsymbol{\alpha}$ of length n then consists of the matrix $\{\alpha_{ij}\}$, $1 \leq j \leq J$, $1 \leq i \leq n$. We further assume that the decoding criterion is to choose the $\mathbf{x}_m$ which maximizes the dot product $\boldsymbol{\alpha} \cdot \mathbf{x}_m$, defined by

$$\boldsymbol{\alpha} \cdot \mathbf{x}_m = \sum_{i=1}^{n} \alpha_{ij(x_{mi})}, \tag{C.1}$$

where $j(x_{mi})$ is defined by

$$x_{j(x_{mi})} = x_{mi}. \tag{C.2}$$

In other words, whatever the value of x_m in the ith place, the corresponding value of α is added to the dot product. Under the conditions that the channel is memoryless, the detector function $\{\alpha_j(y)\}$ is fixed, and the code is chosen from a symmetrized ensemble as in 3.1.4, Equation

C.1 is a sum of n independent, identically distributed random variables whose common moment-generating function is

$$g(-s) = J^{-1} \sum_y \sum_{j=1}^{J} \Pr(y \mid x_j) e^{-s\alpha_j(y)}. \tag{C.3}$$

If the minimum distance of the code is d and if $-1 \le \alpha_j(y) \le 1$, it is easy to prove the first GMD theorem again: There is at most one code word $\mathbf{x}_m$ such that

$$\boldsymbol{\alpha} \cdot \mathbf{x}_m > n - d. \tag{C.4}$$

We also wish to be able to use the second theorem, which permits a decoding algorithm based on already existing erasures-and-errors algorithms. Theorem 3.2 depends on $\boldsymbol{\alpha}$ being the average of some received words $\mathbf{q}_k$ which are suitable for decoding by an erasures-and-errors algorithm—that is, which have in each place either an erasure or an estimate. In the list formulation, an erasure corresponds to a list γ with

$$\gamma_j = 0, \qquad \text{all } j, \tag{C.5}$$

while an estimate of $x_j{}'$ corresponds to a list $\beta_{j'}$ with

$$\beta_{j'j} = \begin{cases} +1, & j = j'; \\ -1, & j \ne j', \end{cases} \tag{C.6}$$

as may be seen by comparison with Equation 3.40 and Equation 3.41. In order that $\boldsymbol{\alpha}$ be an average of some $\mathbf{q}_k$, it is necessary that each component $\{\alpha_j(y)\}$ of $\boldsymbol{\alpha}$ be in the convex hull whose extreme points are γ and the $\beta_{j'}$—that is, that

$$\alpha_j(y) = p_0(y)\gamma_j + \sum_{j'=1}^{J} p_{j'}(y)\beta_{j'j}, \qquad 1 \le j \le J, \tag{C.7}$$

where $0 \le p_{j'}(y) \le 1$ and

$$\sum_{j'=0}^{J} p_{j'}(y) = 1. \tag{C.8}$$

These conditions are sufficient to limit the magnitude of $\alpha_j(y)$ to one, so that the condition which ensures Equation C.4 holds.

The Chernov bound on the probability of a code word $\mathbf{x}_m$ and a received word $\boldsymbol{\alpha}$ such that Equation C.4 fails is minimized by minimizing $g(-s)$, as we saw so many times in Chapter 3. We shall now show that when we minimize Equation C.3 with $\{\alpha_j(y)\}$ constrained by Equation C.7, the resulting $\{\alpha_j(y)\}$ has the form of a GMD list:

$$\alpha_j(y) = (1 - \alpha)\gamma_j + \alpha\beta_{j'j}$$

for some α and j', where $x_{j'}$ is the GMD estimate and α the weight.

Since $e^{-s\alpha_j(y)}$ is a convex upward function of $\alpha_j(y)$, $g(-s)$ is a convex upward function of the $\{\alpha_j(y)\}$, since it is a linear combination of convex upward functions. It follows that a local minimum of $g(-s)$ is the global minimum over the convex space of all $\{\alpha_j(y)\}$ permitted by Equation C.7, so that if we find a point $\{\alpha_{0j}(y)\}$ for which all partial derivatives are zero, then that point is the true minimum.

We rewrite Equation C.7 as

$$\alpha_j(y) = [1 - p(y)]\gamma_j + p(y)\alpha_j'(y) = p(y)\alpha_j'(y), \qquad (C.9)$$

(using Equation C.5), where $\alpha_j'(y)$ is constrained to satisfy

$$\alpha_j'(y) = \sum_{j'=1}^{J} p_{j'}'(y)\beta_{j'j}, \qquad \sum_{j'=1}^{J} p_{j'}'(y) = 1. \qquad (C.10)$$

An equivalent constraint is that $\alpha_j'(y)$ satisfy the conditions

$$-1 \le \alpha_j'(y) \le 1; \qquad (C.11)$$

$$\sum_{j=1}^{J} \alpha_j'(y) = (2 - J). \qquad (C.12)$$

Using a Lagrange multiplier λ to force Equation C.12, we have the partial derivative

$$\frac{\partial}{\partial\alpha_j'(y)}\left[g(-s) + \sum_y \lambda(2 - J)\right] = \frac{\partial}{\partial\alpha_j'(y)} \sum_{j=1}^{J} [\Pr(y \mid x_j)e^{-sp(y)\alpha_j'(y)} + \lambda\alpha_j'(y)]$$

$$= -sp(y)\Pr(y \mid x_j)e^{-sp(y)\alpha_j'(y)} + \lambda, \quad (C.13)$$

from which, using the notation

$$\langle x \rangle = \begin{cases} -1, & x \le -1; \\ x, & -1 \le x \le 1; \\ +1, & x \ge 1, \end{cases}$$

and taking account of Equation C.11, we have

$$\alpha_j'(y) = \langle \lambda' + \frac{1}{sp(y)} \ln \Pr(y \mid x_j) \rangle, \qquad (C.14)$$

where we have combined all terms not depending on j into λ'. We must choose λ' so that Equation C.12 holds; in particular, if the x_j for which $\ln \Pr(y \mid x_j)$ is greatest and second greatest are $x_{j'}$ and $x_{j''}$, and

$$\frac{1}{sp(y)} [\ln \Pr(y \mid x_{j'}) - \ln \Pr(y \mid x_{j''})] \ge 2, \qquad (C.15)$$

then the $\alpha_j'(y)$ which minimizes $g(-s)$ is

$$\alpha_j'(y) = \begin{cases} +1, & j = j' \\ -1, & j \neq j'. \end{cases} \qquad (C.16)$$

Now suppose Equation C.16; then

$$g(-s) = J^{-1} \sum_{y} \left[\Pr(y \mid x_{j'}) e^{-sp(y)} + e^{sp(y)} \sum_{j' \neq j} \Pr(y \mid x_j) \right].$$

(C.17)

Equation C.17 is the minimum of $g(-s)$ with respect to $p(y)$ if

$$\frac{\partial g(-s)}{\partial p(y)} = -s \Pr(y \mid x_{j'}) e^{-sp(y)} + se^{sp(y)} \sum_{j' \neq j} \Pr(y \mid x_j) = 0,$$

(C.18)

which is to say if

$$p(y) = [q(y)],$$

(C.19)

where

$$q(y) = \frac{1}{2s} \ln \frac{\Pr(y \mid x_{j'})}{\sum_{j \neq j'} \Pr(y \mid x_j)}$$

(C.20)

and

$$[x] = \begin{cases} 0, & x \leq 0; \\ x, & 0 \leq x \leq 1; \\ 1, & x \geq 1, \end{cases}$$

to take account of the constraint $0 \leq p(y) \leq 1$.

Suppose that $q(y) < 0$; then $p(y) = 0$ and Equation C.15 holds. Suppose $0 \leq q(y) \leq 1$; then $p(y) = q(y)$, and

$$\frac{1}{sq(y)} [\ln \Pr(y \mid x_{j'}) - \ln \Pr(y \mid x_{j''})]$$
$$= 2 \frac{\ln \Pr(y \mid x_{j'}) - \ln \Pr(y \mid x_{j''})}{\ln \Pr(y \mid x_{j'}) - \ln \sum_{j \neq j'} \Pr(y \mid x_j)} \geq 2, \quad \text{(C.21)}$$

and Equation C.15 holds. Suppose finally that $q(y) > 1$; then $p(y) < q(y)$, and

$$\frac{1}{sp(y)} \ln \frac{\Pr(y \mid x_{j'})}{\Pr(y \mid x_{j''})} > \frac{1}{sq(y)} \ln \frac{\Pr(y \mid x_{j'})}{\Pr(y \mid x_{j''})} \geq 2,$$

as we showed in Equation C.21, so that Equation C.15 holds. It follows that if $\alpha_j'(y)$ is as in Equation C.16 and $p(y)$ as in Equation C.19, then $g(-s)$ is at a local minimum with respect to variations in either, and so at the global minimum. Since Equations C.16 and C.19 correspond to a GMD list with $\hat{x} = x_{j'}$ and $\alpha = p(y)$, and since Equations C.16 and C.19 hold for all outputs y, a GMD list is optimum for all outputs. Therefore within these constraints the added flexibility of list decoding buys us nothing in performance.

Appendix D. Formulas for Computation

In this appendix we derive and discuss the formulas used for the computations of Chapter 5.

D.1 The Outer Decoder

Let us consider first the probability of the outer decoder decoding incorrectly, or failing to decode. We shall let $p_\mathscr{E}$ be the probability that any symbol is in error and p_x be the probability that it is erased.

If the outer decoder does errors-only decoding, $p_x = 0$. Let t_0 be the greatest integer such that $2t_0 < d$; then the probability of decoding error is the probability of $t_0 + 1$ or more symbol errors:

$$\Pr(\mathscr{E}) = \sum_{t=t_0+1}^{n} \binom{n}{t} p_\mathscr{E}^t (1 - p_\mathscr{E})^{n-t}. \tag{D.1}$$

If the outer decoder does erasures-and-errors decoding, the minimum distance is d, and the maximum number of errors corrected is t_0, then the probability of decoding error is the probability that the number of errors t and the number of erasures s satisfy $2t + s \geq d$ or $t \geq t_0 + 1$:

$$\Pr(\mathscr{E}) = \sum_{\substack{t, s \\ 2t+s \geq d \text{ or } t \geq t_0 + 1}} \binom{n}{s, t} p_\mathscr{E}^t p_x^s (1 - p_\mathscr{E} - p_x)^{n-s-t}$$

134

$$= \sum_{t=0}^{t_0} \sum_{s=d-2t}^{n} \binom{n}{s,\,t} p_{\mathscr{E}}^t p_x^s (1 - p_{\mathscr{E}} - p_x)^{n-s-t}$$

$$+ \sum_{t=t_0+1}^{n} \binom{n}{t} p_{\mathscr{E}}^t (1 - p_{\mathscr{E}})^{n-t}. \quad \text{(D.2)}$$

For fixed t, we can lowerbound an expression of the form

$$\sum_{s=t_1}^{n} \binom{n}{s,\,t} p_{\mathscr{E}}^t p_x^s (1 - p_{\mathscr{E}} - p_x)^{n-s-t} \quad \text{(D.3)}$$

by

$$\sum_{s=t_1}^{t_2+1} \binom{n}{s,\,t} p_{\mathscr{E}}^t p_x^s (1 - p_{\mathscr{E}} - p_x)^{n-s-t}. \quad \text{(D.4)}$$

To upperbound Equation D.3, we write it as

$$\sum_{s=t_1}^{t_2} \binom{n}{s,\,t} p_{\mathscr{E}}^t p_x^s (1 - p_{\mathscr{E}} - p_x)^{n-s-t}$$

$$+ \sum_{s=t_2+1}^{n} \binom{n}{s,\,t} p_{\mathscr{E}}^t p_x^s (1 - p_{\mathscr{E}} - p_x)^{n-s-t}. \quad \text{(D.5)}$$

Since the ratio of the $(s + 1)$st to the sth term in the latter series is

$$\frac{(n - s - t) p_x}{(s + 1)(1 - p_{\mathscr{E}} - p_x)} \le \frac{(n - t - t_2) p_x}{t_2 (1 - p_{\mathscr{E}} - p_x)} = a,$$

Equation D.5 can be upperbounded by

$$\sum_{s=t_1}^{t_2} \binom{n}{s,\,t} p_{\mathscr{E}}^t p_x^s (1 - p_{\mathscr{E}} - p_x)^{n-s-t} + \binom{n}{t_2 + 1,\,t} p_{\mathscr{E}}^t p_x^{t_2+1}$$

$$\times (1 - p_{\mathscr{E}} - p_x)^{n-t-t_2-1} \sum_{s'\ge 0} a^{s'}$$

$$= \sum_{s=t_1}^{t_2} \binom{n}{s,\,t} p_{\mathscr{E}}^t p_x^s (1 - p_{\mathscr{E}} - p_x)^{n-s-t} + \frac{1}{1-a} \binom{n}{t_2 + 1,\,t} p_{\mathscr{E}}^t p_x^{t_2+1}$$

$$\times (1 - p_{\mathscr{E}} - p_x)^{n-t-t_2-1}. \quad \text{(D.6)}$$

By choosing t_2 large enough, the lower and upper bounds of Equations D.4 and D.6 may be made as close as desired. In the program of Chapter 5, we let t_2 be large enough so that the bounds were within one per cent of each other. Both Equations D.1 and D.2 can then be upperbounded and approximated by Equation D.6.

D.2   The Inner Decoder

If the inner decoder is set to do errors-only decoding, the inner decoder corrects as many errors as it can (t_0). Whenever the actual number of errors exceeds t_0, the inner decoder will either fail to decode or decode in error, but either of these events constitutes a symbol error to the outer decoder. If the probability of symbol error for the inner decoder is p_0, then

$$p_{\mathscr{E}} = \sum_{t=t_0+1}^{n} \binom{n}{t} p_0^t (1 - p_0)^{n-t}. \qquad \text{(D.7)}$$

Equation D.7 can be upperbounded and approximated by Equation D.6.

If the outer decoder is set for erasures-and-errors decoding, the inner decoder is set to correct whenever there are apparently t_1 or fewer errors, where $t_1 \leq t_0$; otherwise it signals an erasure. If there are more than t_1 errors, the decoder will either erase or decode incorrectly, so that

$$p_{\mathscr{E}} + p_x = \sum_{t=t_1+1}^{n} \binom{n}{t} p_0^t (1 - p_0)^{n-t};$$

ordinarily t_1 is set so that $p_{\mathscr{E}} \ll p_x$, so that p_x is upperbounded and approximated by

$$p_x \leq \sum_{t=t_1+1}^{n} \binom{n}{t} p_0^t (1 - p_0)^{n-t}, \qquad \text{(D.8)}$$

which in turn is upperbounded and approximated by Equation D.6.

Estimating $p_{\mathscr{E}}$ turns out to be a knottier problem. Of course, if the minimum distance of the inner code is d, no error can occur unless the number of symbol errors is at least $d - t_1$, so that

$$p_{\mathscr{E}} \leq \sum_{t=d-t_1}^{n} \binom{n}{t} p_0^t (1 - p_0)^{n-t}.$$

This is a valid upper bound but a very weak estimate of $p_{\mathscr{E}}$, since in general many fewer than the total of $\binom{n}{t}$ t-error patterns will cause errors; most will be detected and result in erasures. A tighter bound for $p_{\mathscr{E}}$ depends, however, on knowledge of the distribution of weights in the inner code, which is in general difficult to calculate.

We can get a weak bound on the number N_w of code words of weight w in any linear code on $GF(q)$ of length n and minimum distance d, as follows. Let t_0 be the greatest integer such that $2t_0 < d$. The total number of code words of weight $w - t_0$ distance t_0 from a code word of weight w is $\binom{w}{t_0}$, since to get such a word we may change any t_0 of the

w nonzero symbols in the word to zeroes. The total number of words of weight $w - t_0$ distance t_0 from some code word of weight w is then

$$\binom{w}{t_0} N_w$$

and all of these are distinct, since no word can be distance t_0 from two different code words. But this number cannot exceed the total number of words of weight $w - t_0$:

$$\binom{n}{w - t_0}(q - 1)^{w - t_0}.$$

Therefore

$$N_w \le \frac{n! t_0! (q - 1)^{w - t_0}}{w! (n - w + t_0)!}. \tag{D.9}$$

A decoding error will occur when the error pattern is distance t_1 or less from some code word. The total number of words distance k from some code word of weight w is

$$\sum_{\substack{i, j, l \\ i + j + l = k}} \binom{n - w}{l}(q - 1)^l \binom{w}{i, j}(q - 2)^i,$$

since all such words can be obtained by changing any l of the $n - w$ zeroes to any of the $(q - 1)$ nonzero elements, any i of the w nonzero elements to any of the other $(q - 2)$ nonzero elements, and any j of the remaining nonzero elements to zeroes, where $i + j + l = k$. The weight of the resulting word for a particular i, j, l will be $w + l - j$, so that the probability of getting a word distance k from a particular code word of weight w is

$$\sum_{\substack{i, j, l \\ i + j + l = k}} \binom{n - w}{l}(q - 1)^l \binom{w}{i, j}(q - 2)^i \left(\frac{p_0}{q - 1}\right)^{w + l - j}(1 - p_0)^{n - w - l + j}.$$

Summing over all words of all weights $w \ge d$ and all $k \le t_1$, and substituting $j = k - i - l \ge 0$,

$$p_{\mathscr{E}} = \sum_{w = d}^{n} \sum_{k = 0}^{t_1} \sum_{i = 0}^{k} \sum_{l = 0}^{k - i} N_w$$

$$\times \frac{(n - w)! w! (q - 1)^{-w + k - i - l}(q - 2)^i p_0^{w + 2l + i - k}(1 - p_0)^{n - w - 2l - i + k}}{l! (n - w - l)! i! (k - i - l)! (w - k + l)!}.$$

Interchanging sums, substituting the upper bound of Equation D.9 for N_w, and writing the ranges of w, k, i, and l more suggestively, we have

$$p_{\mathscr{E}} \le \sum_{k \le t_1} \sum_{i \ge 0} \sum_{l \ge 0} \sum_{w \ge d}$$

$$\times \frac{n! t_0! (n-w)! (q-1)^{k-l-i-t_0} (q-2)^i p_0^{w+2l+i-k} (1-p_0)^{n-w-2l-i+k}}{l! (n-w-l)! i! (k-l-i)! (w-k+l)! (n-w+t_0)!}.$$

We now show that the dominant term in this sum is that specified by $k = t_1$, $i = 0$, $l = 0$, and $w = d$, and in fact that the whole series is bounded by

$$p_{\mathscr{E}} \le C_1 C_2 C_3 C_4 \frac{n! t_0! (q-1)^{t_1-t_0} p_0^{d-t_1} (1-p_0)^{n-d+t_1}}{t_1! (d-t_1)! (n-d+t_0)!} \qquad \text{(D.10)}$$

where

$$C_1 = \frac{1}{1-a_1}, \qquad a_1 = \frac{p_0}{1-p_0} \frac{n-d+t_0}{d-t_1+1};$$

$$C_2 = \frac{1}{1-a_2}, \qquad a_2 = \left(\frac{p_0}{1-p_0}\right)^2 \frac{1}{q-1} \frac{(n-d)t_1}{d-t_1+1};$$

$$C_3 = \frac{1}{1-a_3}, \qquad a_3 = \frac{p_0}{1-p_0} \frac{q-2}{q-1} t_1;$$

$$C_4 = \frac{1}{1-a_4}, \qquad a_4 = \frac{p_0}{1-p_0} \frac{1}{q-1} \frac{t_1}{d-t_1+1},$$

and it is assumed that the constants a_m are less than one. This result follows from repeated bounding of the series by the first and dominant term multiplied by a series of the form

$$\sum_{n \ge 0} a_m^n = \frac{1}{1-a_m}.$$

For example, the ratio of the $(w+1)$st to the wth term is

$$\frac{p_0}{1-p_0} \frac{n-w-l}{n-w} \frac{n-w+t_0}{w-k+l+1} \le a_1,$$

since $w \ge d$, $k \le t_1$, and $l \ge 0$.

The ratio of the $(l+1)$st to the lth term is

$$\left(\frac{p_0}{1-p_0}\right)^2 \frac{1}{q-1} \frac{n-w-l}{l+1} \frac{k-l-i}{w-k+l+1} \le a_2;$$

of the $(i+1)$st to the ith:

$$\frac{p_0}{1-p_0} \frac{q-2}{q-1} \frac{k-l-i}{i+1} \le a_3;$$

and of the $(k-1)$st to the kth:

$$\frac{p_0}{1-p_0}\frac{1}{q-1}\frac{k-l-i}{w-k+l+1} \le a_4.$$

The bound on p_δ of Equation D.10 is a valid upper bound, but not a good approximation, since Equation D.9 is a weak bound for N_w.

D.3 Modulation on a Gaussian Channel

We contemplate sending one of $M = 2^K$ biorthogonal signals over an unlimited bandwidth additive white Gaussian noise channel. A well-known model[1] for such a transmission is the following. The M signals are represented by the M $(M/2)$-dimensional vectors x_m, $1 \le m \le M/2$ or $-1 \ge m \ge -M/2$, which are the vectors with zeroes in all places but the $|m|$th, and in that place have $\pm\sqrt{E_w}$ according to whether $m = \pm|m|$, where E_w is the transmitted energy per waveform. (These vectors correspond to what would be observed at the outputs of a bank of $M/2$ matched filters if the waveforms they represent, uncorrupted by noise, were the input.)

The actual, noisy outputs of the matched filter bank are represented by the $(M/2)$-dimensional vector

$$\mathbf{y} = (y_1, y_2, \cdots, y_{M/2}).$$

If the noise has two-sided spectral density $N_0/2$, then the noise energy per dimension is $N_0/2$, and

$$\Pr(\mathbf{y}\mid x_m) = (\pi N_0)^{M/4}\exp-\sum_{i=1}^{M/2}\frac{(y_i-x_{mi})^2}{N_0}.$$

Interpreting

$$\sum_{i=1}^{M/2}(y_i-x_{mi})^2$$

as the Euclidean distance between the vectors $\mathbf{y}$ and x_m, we see that the maximum likelihood decision rule is to choose that input closest in Euclidean distance to the received signal.

The case $M = 4$ is illustrated in Figure D.1, where we have drawn in the lines marking the boundaries of the decision regions. There is perfect symmetry between the four inputs. If one of them, say $(\sqrt{E_w}, 0)$, is selected, the probability of error is the probability that the received signal will lie outside the decision region that contains $(\sqrt{E_w}, 0)$. If we

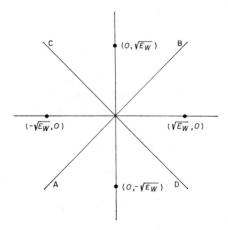

Figure D.1   Decision regions for four biorthogonal signals.

let E_1 be the event that the received signal falls on the other side of the line AB from $(\sqrt{E_w}, 0)$, and E_2, that it falls on the other side of CD, then it can readily be shown by a 45° coordinate rotation that E_1 and E_2 are independent, and that each has probability

$$p = \frac{1}{\sqrt{\pi N_0}} \int_{\sqrt{E_w/2}}^{\infty} e^{-y^2/N_0}\, dy$$

$$= \frac{1}{\sqrt{2\pi}} \int_{\sqrt{E_w/N_0}}^{\infty} e^{-z^2/2}\, dz = \Phi\left(\sqrt{\frac{E_w}{N_0}}\right). \qquad (D.11)$$

The probability that neither occurs is $(1 - p)^2$, so that the probability that at least one occurs, which is the probability of error, is

$$q = 2p - p^2. \qquad (D.12)$$

When $M > 4$, the symmetry between the inputs still obtains, so let us suppose the transmission of

$$\mathbf{x}_1 = (\sqrt{E_w}, 0, \cdots, 0).$$

Let E_j, $2 \le j \le M/2$, be defined as the event in which the received vector is closer to one of the three vectors $\mathbf{x}_{-1}$, $\mathbf{x}_j$, or $\mathbf{x}_{-j}$ than to $\mathbf{x}_1$. Then the event $\mathscr{E}$ of an error is the union of these events

$$\mathscr{E} = \bigcup_{j=2}^{M/2} E_j.$$

But the probability of any one of these events is q. Thus, by the union bound,

$$p_0 = \Pr(\mathscr{E}) \le \sum_{j=2}^{M/2} \Pr(E_j) = (M/2 - 1)q. \qquad (D.13)$$

When the signal-to-noise ratio per transmitted waveform E_w/N_0 is large, the bound of Equations D.11, D.12, and D.13 becomes tight. To calculate Φ, we use an approximation of Hastings.[2] Viterbi[3] has calculated the exact value of p_0 for $3 \le K \le 10$; we have fitted curves to his data in the low signal-to-noise range, and used the above bound elsewhere, so that over the whole range p_0 is given correctly to within one per cent. When $K \ge 11$, the union bound is used for all signal-to-noise ratios.

Finally, we have the problem of bounding the erasure and error probabilities, when the detector erases whenever the magnitude of some matched filter output is not at least D greater than that of any other. Figure D.2 illustrates the decision and erasure regions, again for $M = 4$.

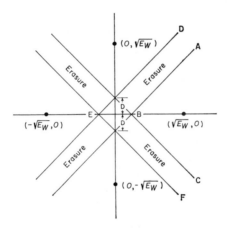

Figure D.2 Addition of an erasure region.

It is clear that the probability of not decoding correctly is computed exactly as before, with $\sqrt{E_w}$ replaced by $\sqrt{E_w} - D$; this probability overbounds and approximates the erasure probability. The probability of error is overbounded, not tightly, by the probability of falling outside the shaded line DEF, which probability is computed as before with $\sqrt{E_w}$ replaced by $\sqrt{E_w} + D$.

When $M > 4$, the union bound arguments presented above are still valid, again with $\sqrt{E_w}$ replaced by $\sqrt{E_w} - D$ for erasure probability and by $\sqrt{E_w} + D$ for error probability.

The case in which $M = 2$ is trivial.

References

1. S. W. Golomb *et al.*, *Digital Communications with Space Applications*, Prentice-Hall, Englewood Cliffs, New Jersey, 1964.
2. D. Hastings, *Approximations for Digital Computers*, Princeton University Press, Princeton, New Jersey, 1955.
3. A. Viterbi, in Golomb, *op. cit.*, Appendix 4.

Author Index

(Note: all authors quoted in the text appear in this index, with the page where quoted. Page numbers in **boldface** indicate a complete reference.)

Artin, E., 12, **34**
Assmus, E. F., Jr., 21, **34**

Bartee, T. C., 26, **34**, 120, **129**
Berlekamp, E. R., 27, 57, 106, **113**
Bose, R. C., 30, **34**

Carmichael, R. D., 12, 25, **34**
Chernov, H., 47, **62**
Chien, R. T., 121, 122, **129**
Codex Corp., **11**

Fano, R. M., 47, **62**, 110, 112, **113**
Forney, G. D., Jr., **vii**, 114, **129**

Gallager, R. G., 11, 47, **62**, 67, **90**, 106, 110, 112, **113**
Gleason, A. M., 21, **34**
Golomb, S. W., 9, **11**, 100, **105**, 139, **142**
Gorenstein, D., 114, 117, **129**

Hackett, C. M., Jr., 53, **62**
Hardy, G. H., 70, **90**

Hastings, D., 141, **142**
Hocquenghem, A., 30, **34**

Jacobs, I. M., **11**

Kasami, T., 21, 25, **34**, 43, **62**
Kohlenberg, A., 20

Lin, S., 21, 25, **34**
Littlewood, J. E., 70, **90**

MacWilliams, J., 25, **34**, 43, **62**
Massey, J. L., **11**, 122, **129**
Mattson, H. F., 21, 28, 33, **34**
Mitchell, M. E., 9, **11**, 43, **62**

Peterson, W. W., 12, 21, 25, 26, 33, **34**, 120, **129**
Pinsker, M. S., 88, **90**
Pólya, G., 70, **90**
Prange, E., 17, **34**, 43, **62**

Ray-Chaudhuri, D. K., 30, **34**

143

Reed, I. S., 21, 28, **34**

Schneider, D. I., 26, **34,** 120, **129**
Shannon, C. E., 1, **11,** 47, **62,** 106, **113**
Singleton, R. C., 18, **34**
Slepian, D., 16, **34**
Solomon, G., 21, 28, 33, **34**

Viterbi, A. J., 9, **11,** 141, **142**

Weaver, W., **11**
Wozencraft, J. M., **11**

Zierler, N., 27, **34,** 114, 117, **129**
Ziv, J., 88, **90**

Subject Index

BCH codes, 5, 6, 12–33, 43, 57, 92, 93, 100
  asymptotic performance of, 33
  decoding of, 114–129
  definition, 30
  number of information symbols in, 30–33
Binary signals, geometric representation of, 36
Bursts, 10, 11

Capacity, definition, 3
Channel, 1
  binary symmetric, 67, 92–99
  discrete memoryless, 2
  equierror, 71, 75–77, 92–99
  Gaussian, *see* Gaussian channel
  telltale, 72, 77–78
Characteristic of a field, 15
Chernov bounds, 43, 47–51, 58–59, 84–87, 131–133
Codes, BCH, *see* BCH codes
  biorthogonal, 100
  block, 2, 5
  convolutional, 4, 10–11
  cyclic, 22–23
  cyclic RS, 22–25

cyclic-plus, 24, 26, 30, 119
inner, 5
linear, 4, 16–21
maximum (maximum-distance), 18–21
outer, 5
Reed-Solomon, *see* Reed-Solomon codes
Coding theorem, 1–4, 9, 10, 16, 64–69, 106–113
  for superchannels, 63–83
Complexity, 4, 6, 9–10, 26–27, 43, 46, 57, 61, 88, 119–121
Concatenation, burst resistance of, 10
  computed performance of, 91–105
  with convolutional codes, 10
  idea of, 5–6
  theoretical performance of, 63–90
Convexity of error exponent, 69–70

Decision region, 38, 139–141
Decoder, definition, 2, 37
  likelihood, *see* Word correlator
Decoding, conditional, 37, 39, 43
  erasures-and-errors, *see* Erasures-and-errors decoding

145

Decoding, (*continued*)
  errors-only, *see* Errors-only decoding
  exhaustive, 37
  generalized minimum distance, *see* Generalized minimum distance decoding
  Hamming distance, 40–43
  list, 6, 9, 59–61, 130–133
  maximum likelihood, *see* Maximum likelihood decoding
  sequential, 4, 11
  threshold, 11
Demodulator, 7–8
Detector, 7–8, 36–37, 49–50
  likelihood, 7–8, 36
Distance, Euclidean, 37, 139
  generalized, 43
  Hamming, 17, 40–41
  minimum, 17

Efficiency of concatenation, 82–83
Elementary symmetric functions, 116
Encoder, for cyclic-plus codes, 26
  definition, 2
  for linear codes, 18
Erasures, 6, 7, 9, 42, 59, 60
Erasures-and-errors decoding, 42–43, 44, 85–86
  with nonbinary signals, 59
  optimum detector for, 49–50
  performance on a Gaussian channel of, 52–54
Error exponent, 66
  convexity of, 69–70
  lower-bound, 3
  normalized, 68
  true, 74
  upper-bound, 4
Errors-only decoding, 39–43, 44, 84–85
  with nonbinary signals, 59
  optimum detector for, 49–50
  performance on a Gaussian channel of, 52–53
Estimate, 55, 60
Exponents, concatenation, 6, 75–83

Fields, finite, 12–16, 23
  locator, 30
  symbol, 30

Gaussian channel, 51–55, 139–141
  concatenation exponents for, 80–81
  concatenation on, 99–105
  error exponent for, 67–68
Generalized minimum distance decoding, 6, 7, 9, 35–62, 63, 92, 130
  algorithm for, 125–129
  compared with maximum likelihood, 55, 61
  complexity of, 57
  in concatenation, 86–88
  definition, 43–44
  with nonbinary signals, 55–59
  optimum detector for, 49–50
  performance on a Gaussian channel of, 52–55
  use of an erasures-and-errors decoder in, 44–46
Generators of a linear code, 18
Geometric representation of binary signals, 36
$GF(4)$, tables for, 15

Information packet, 9, 63–64
Information sets, 17–19, 21
  in BCH codes, 32
Information symbols in BCH codes, number of, 30–33
Interlacing, 10, 28

Length, normalized, 67
  over-all, 75
List decoding, 6, 9, 59–61, 130–133
Locator, 21
Log likelihood ratio, bit, 36, 51
  estimate, 59
  symbol, 58
Maximum likelihood decoding, 3, 7, 37–39, 63
  with erasures, 106–107
  performance on a Gaussian channel of, 51–52
Memory, channels with, 10
Modulation, 7–8
Moment-generating function, 49

Null zone, 42

Permutations on RS codes, 22–25
Place (in a word), 16

Rate, 2
  dimensionless, 2, 18
  normalized, 67
  over-all, 75
Reed-Solomon codes, 6, 11, 12–33, 57, 63, 92, 100–105
  cyclic and cyclic-plus, 22–25
  decoding of, 114–129
  definition, 21
  implementation of, 26–29
  as outer codes, 83–88
  permutations on, 25
  shortened, 27–28

Scrambling, *see* Interlacing
Sequential decoding, 4, 11
Sets (of places in a word), 17
  information, *see* Information sets
Signal-to-noise ratio, per information bit, 67
  per transmitted bit, 51

Subfield, 15
Superchannel, 5, 63–64
  equierror, 71
  GMD equierror, 72
Symmetry, between inputs, 47–48, 58
  between outputs other than estimate, 74
Syndromes, 115–116

Threshold decoding, 11

Van der Monde-like matrices, 22, 32, 117–118, 128

Weight, of binary output, 36
  of nonbinary output, 55
  of word, 16, 17
Weight distribution, bound on, 136–137
  of maximum codes, 19–21
Word correlator, 8–9, 60, 100